423 ILLUSTRATIONS IN FULL COLOR

BUTTERFLIES
AND MOTHS

*A GUIDE TO THE MORE COMMON
AMERICAN SPECIES*

by ROBERT T. MITCHELL
and
HERBERT S. ZIM

ILLUSTRATED BY ANDRE DURENCEAU

A GOLDEN NATURE GUIDE

GOLDEN PRESS ✕ **NEW YORK**

FOREWORD

This book presents an introduction to American butterflies and moths. So numerous are North American species that only about three per cent have been included, but these were selected to include the most common, widespread, important, or unusual kinds. Special attention has been given to immature forms and to range maps which show distribution.

Andre Durenceau deserves our special thanks for his magnificent art, so painstakingly done. The technical assistance of William D. Field has also been invaluable. The authors are also gratefully indebted to other specialists at the Smithsonian Institution, especially J. F. Gates Clarke, Head Curator, Dept. of Entomology, and to H. W. Capps and E. L. Todd. Among numerous others who contributed are W. A. Anderson, T. L. Bissell, J. H. Fales, R. S. Simmons, and several entomologists of the U.S. Forest Service.

R.T.M.
H.S.Z.

Library of Congress Catalog Card Number: 64-24907

CONTENTS

INTRODUCING LEPIDOPTERA

Butterflies and moths are most numerous in the tropics, but temperate areas have a bountiful supply of many species. Like all insects, they have three main body regions (head, thorax, and abdomen), three pairs of jointed legs, and one pair of antennae. Most have two pairs of wings. A few are wingless.

Insects that possess certain basic structures in common are classified into large groups or orders. Butterflies and moths are members of the order Lepidoptera, derived from the Greek *lepidos* for scales and *ptera* for wings. Their scaled wings distinguish them as a group from all other insects. When butterflies and moths are handled, the scales rub off as colored powder. Under a microscope, the colors and forms of the scales are amazing.

Lepidoptera is the largest order of insects next to Coleoptera (beetles). Beetles are estimated at about 280,000 species; Lepidoptera at 120,000, with about 10,000 species in North America. Lepidoptera is usually divided into three suborders: first, *Jugatae*, with about 250 primitive species that somewhat resemble caddisflies; second, *Frenatae*, most moths; and, third, *Rhopalocera*, the butterflies and skippers.

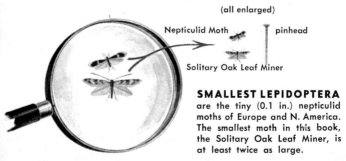

(all enlarged)

Nepticulid Moth — pinhead

Solitary Oak Leaf Miner

SMALLEST LEPIDOPTERA are the tiny (0.1 in.) nepticulid moths of Europe and N. America. The smallest moth in this book, the Solitary Oak Leaf Miner, is at least twice as large.

butterfly scales

moth scales

SCALES cover the wings of all Lepidoptera in overlapping rows. Moth scales are variable, sometimes "hairy." Butterfly scales are more uniform. Some, on males, are modified into scent scales.

The suborder Rhopalocera is divided into two super-families, *Papilionoidea*, which includes 19 families of butterflies, and *Hesperioidea*, two families of skippers. Butterflies and skippers are easy to distinguish by the shape and position of their antennae (pp. 19 and 74).

The suborder Frenatae includes about fifty families of North American moths. No single feature will enable one to tell a moth from a butterfly or skipper, but a frenulum (p. 81) on the hindwing of most moths extends to the forewing, holding the wings together. The presence and position of simple eyes (ocelli) and leg spines, the nature of the antennae, and the shape and venation of the wings are used in moth identification. To make veins more visible for study, the wings can be moistened with alcohol, which does not harm them.

Families are subdivided into genera (plural of genus). Each genus contains one or more species. A species has a double scientific name, such as *Pieris rapae* for the Cabbage Butterfly. *Pieris* is the name of the genus; *rapae* is the species name. See pp. 154-157 for scientific names of species illustrated in this book.

5

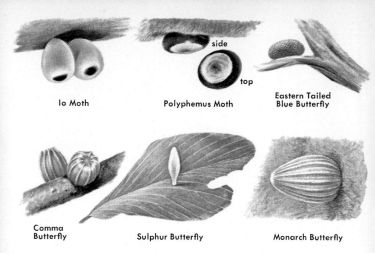

Io Moth

Polyphemus Moth
side
top

Eastern Tailed
Blue Butterfly

Comma
Butterfly

Sulphur Butterfly

Monarch Butterfly

EGGS OF BUTTERFLIES AND MOTHS.

LIFE HISTORIES In the simple growth pattern of primitive insects, of which silverfish are examples, the individual that hatches from the egg is a miniature replica of the adult. Its appearance does not change much as it grows. The orders containing true bugs, aphids, dragonflies, grasshoppers, and others show a more advanced pattern. The immature insect (nymph) usually resembles the adult, though not always, and the immature stages lack functional wings.

Lepidoptera (and other orders, accounting for nearly 90% of all insect species) develop by a complete metamorphosis which is characterized by four distinct stages. These are shown for the Gypsy Moth on p. 136. The egg hatches into a larva (the caterpillar of butterflies and moths), which feeds, grows, and molts several times before transforming into a pupa. After a period of time, a winged adult emerges.

EGGS of Lepidoptera vary greatly in size and shape. Many are smooth and spherical, but some kinds are flattened, conical, spindle- or barrel-shaped. Most eggs are ornamented with ribs, pits, or grooves, or with networks of fine ridges. Each egg has a small hole through which it is fertilized.

The female may lay eggs singly, in small clusters, or in one egg mass. Depending on the species, the eggs are sometimes dropped at random. More often they are deposited in some definite pattern (often in rows) on the plant that will serve as food for the larva. The eggs are often adhesive and stick to the plant when laid. Some eggs are laid on the ground, and the newly hatched larvae must seek their food plants. Eggs laid during the summer are usually thin-coated; those that overwinter before hatching have a thicker outer coat and are sometimes covered by "hair" from the moth. They may also be covered by a foamy layer, as with the Tent Caterpillar, shown below.

Most eggs hatch in a few days. The larva, which can frequently be seen inside the egg just before hatching, eats its way out and sometimes also eats the eggshell. Some larvae are fully developed in eggs laid in the fall but hibernate in the egg and do not hatch until spring.

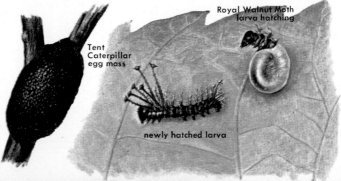

Royal Walnut Moth larva hatching

Tent Caterpillar egg mass

newly hatched larva

LARVAE are usually ravenous feeders. Some kinds mature in a week; others take several months. Most larvae feed actively until they go into the pupal stage. Some become dormant, or estivate, during the dry months of summer. Others hibernate, including some that overwinter as newly hatched or partly grown larvae.

All Lepidoptera larvae are caterpillars, though some are known as slugs, worms, or borers. They feed on leaves, flowers, and fruits of plants, occasionally boring into stems and wood. Some species are scavengers, and a smaller number feed on insects, especially on plant lice and scale insects. Another small group feeds on animal products such as wool, silk, or feathers.

Some caterpillars are green, with skin so thin and transparent that the color of the chloroplasts in their plant food shows through. Many more are brightly marked with bold patterns. Some have knobs, bumps, horns, spines, and hairs. Most species are smooth skinned, but hairiness ranges from a trace of hair to a complete furry covering. In some species, such as the Io Moth, Saddleback, Flannel Moth, and Brown-tail Moth, the hairs and spines are poisonous and irritating to the human skin. North American caterpillars range in length from less than 0.2 inches to nearly 6 inches.

SOME UNUSUAL
CATERPILLARS

American Copper
Butterfly

Tiger Swallowtail

Great Spangled
Fritillary

As a caterpillar grows, it sheds its skin, or molts. This permits another period of growth. The larva in these periods between molts is called an instar. Early instars may differ from older larvae in color, markings, and in their shape.

The caterpillar, like the adult, has three body regions —head, thorax, and abdomen. The head, formed of five or six fused segments, has a pair of short antennae. On each side of the head are pairs of ocelli, or simple eyes, usually in a semicircle. The mouthparts include a pair of strong, conspicuous jaws (mandibles), an upper lip (labrum), a lower lip (labium), and two segmented sensory structures (palpi). The labium most often has a spinneret used for making silk filaments.

On each of the three segments of the thorax is a pair of short, jointed legs ending in claws. On each side of the first thoracic segment is a spiracle, an opening for breathing, the only pair on the thorax.

The abdomen, usually composed of ten segments, bears two to five pairs of short, fleshy prolegs, most often on segments 3, 4, 5, 6, and 10. Segment 10 bears the last and largest pair, the anal prolegs. Spiracles also occur on each side of the first eight abdominal segments; in many species the area around these openings is colored.

Saddleback Moth

Unicorn Moth

Woolly Bear (Isabella Moth)

Linden Looper

9

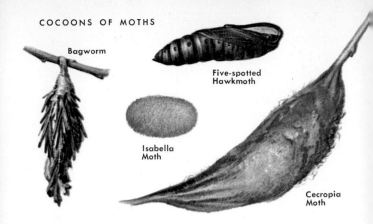

Bagworm

Five-spotted
Hawkmoth

Isabella
Moth

Cecropia
Moth

PUPAE are the resting forms in which the larvae transform into adults. Most butterflies and moths in temperate regions spend the winter as pupae, though the pupal stage of some species lasts for only a few days. The transformation which goes on in the pupal stage is exceedingly complex. The larva loses its prolegs in a prepupal stage; later its mouthparts change from chewing mandibles to a long proboscis (if present in the adult), wings develop, and reproductive organs form. Some of these changes are foreshadowed even in the larva, but they are not completed until the pupal stage. External factors, such as temperature and moisture, may trigger the changes, but the actual transformation is caused by hormones. The pupa may rest for some time before the actual transformation into the adult occurs.

The butterfly larva attaches itself to a firm support before changing into the naked pupa, known as a chrysalis. Larvae of some moths burrow into the ground and pupate; others pupate amid dead leaves, grass, or in debris on the ground.

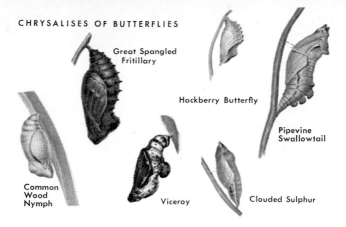

CHRYSALISES OF BUTTERFLIES

Great Spangled
Fritillary

Hackberry Butterfly

Pipevine
Swallowtail

Common
Wood
Nymph

Viceroy

Clouded Sulphur

Many moth larvae spin some kind of a cocoon that surrounds the pupa. The cocoons of silkworm moths and many others are capsules of silk filaments. Some larvae add twigs, leaves, bits of grass, and other materials to the outside of the cocoon, and build the walls in a double or triple layer. The Promethea Moth and others use an entire leaf as the outer layer of the cocoon. This is attached to the food plant by silk filaments. So through the long winter months, the cocoon hangs from the twig like a dead leaf.

Hairy caterpillars often mix hairs with the silk in their cocoons. Some build an escape hatch through which the adult can later emerge; other moths secrete a fluid that softens the pupal silk when it is time to leave. Others have spines with which they can cut or tear their way out. Moths take considerable time to emerge; butterflies come out quickly. Both emerge with soft, limp, moist wings which slowly expand as fluids are pumped through the veins. Later the veins harden, providing a rigid support for the wing membrane.

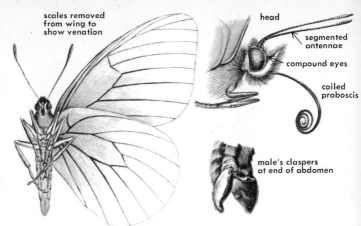

scales removed from wing to show venation

head

segmented antennae

compound eyes

coiled proboscis

male's claspers at end of abdomen

AN ADULT butterfly or moth has a pair of segmented antennae and a pair of large, rounded, compound eyes on its head. Many moths also have a pair of simple eyes. Butterflies and many moths have a coiled proboscis, which unrolls into a long sucking tube through which the adult feeds on nectar and other fluids. This tube may be as long as the adult's body.

Each of the three segments of the thorax bears a pair of five-jointed legs. Some groups of butterflies have the first pair of legs reduced, and females of the bagworm moths lack legs entirely. Most butterflies and moths have two pairs of membranous wings attached to the 2nd and 3rd segments of the thorax; a few kinds are wingless. The vein pattern of the wings is important in identification.

At the end of the ten-segmented abdomen are the sex organs. They are used in the accurate identification of most species. The female's abdomen is usually larger than the male's. The latter can be identified by the claspers of the sex organs which protrude as plate-like structures at the end of the last segment.

ACTIVITIES WITH LEPIDOPTERA

Each year thousands of people become interested in butterflies and moths. They collect, mount, and identify specimens. Some gather caterpillars and rear them, following one insect through its fascinating life history. Detailed observations, notes, and photographs on just one species may lead to new discoveries, for data on many species are lacking, especially on the larvae. Perhaps you can locate a club or group of interested amateurs. If not, encourage someone to join you in the hobby of collecting, studying, and rearing Lepidoptera. Collecting is permitted almost anywhere except in national parks. Respect private property. Ask first, and permission to collect will usually be granted.

COLLECTING is essential in studying butterflies and moths. Usually adults are collected while feeding at flowers or bait. They are rarely caught on the wing. The specimen is quickly transferred to a killing jar. Later it is mounted, spread, labeled, and catalogued.

Better specimens can be obtained, and much more learned in the process, by rearing your own caterpillars. Look for them on plants; chewed leaves are a sign they are present. Some feed only at night; many feed on the undersides of the leaves. Larvae are reared easily in large cans. Keep each kind of larva in a separate can. Give them the kind of leaves on which they were feeding when found. Put only a few larvae in each can and do not stuff the can with leaves. Clean daily and add fresh leaves as needed. Species that form cocoons are the easiest to rear. Caterpillars will pupate on twigs or on the bottom of the can. Pupae need some moisture to survive but should not be wet. They can be stored in containers with a layer of moist peat moss or soil at the bottom.

light box

NIGHT COLLECTING A lamp set in front of a hanging sheet or a homemade light box will often yield night-flying moths.

lightweight net

COLLECTING NETS can be purchased from scientific supply houses or made at home. Use a lightweight net to catch butterflies and moths on plants. A heavier muslin net is used in "sweeping" grass and bushes.

rearing or breeding cage

muslin net

When movement and change in appearance of a pupa indicates the adult is about to emerge, put it in a cage. Make one about a foot in diameter from a rolled section of wire screen or ¼ inch hardware cloth. Paper plates make good tops and bottoms. A variety of sizes to meet all your needs can be quickly, easily, and cheaply made.

Caged females kept outdoors may attract males. If a male is added he will mate with the female and fertilize her eggs. Most females caught outdoors have already mated. Silk moths, tiger moths, and others that do not feed as adults will lay eggs soon after mating. Butterflies and moths that feed as adults will lay eggs over a longer period. Some of these species will die without laying eggs if not given the proper food plant.

Eggs can be kept in flat tins or in small plastic or glass containers. Tops should fit tightly to prevent the tiny larvae from escaping when they hatch. Then, fresh food plants are needed promptly.

temporary killing jar

permanent killing jar

commercial spreading board

homemade spreading board

insect pins and labels

KILLING JARS can be made by pouring about a half inch of plaster of Paris into a wide-mouthed jar. After the plaster has dried thoroughly, saturate it with ethyl acetate or carbon tetrachloride, pouring off the excess liquid. When the jar loses its killing power, repeat the chemical treatment. Strips of rough paper placed in the jar will reduce damage to specimens. For temporary use, try a jar containing a few paper strips moistened with one of these chemicals. Specimens too stiff for mounting can be relaxed by placing them in a tight jar containing a layer of moist sand covered with a piece of cardboard.

SPREADING BOARDS are made of soft wood with a center channel into which the body of the specimen fits. Pin the specimen through its thorax and spread its wings at a right angle to the body. To reduce the loss of scales, use forceps or an insect pin. Never use fingers. Pin the wings in place with paper strips. Allow several days for drying. Spreading boards can be made at home. Study a purchased model first.

INSECT PINS are made of special rust-resistant steel. They come in several sizes. Size 3 can be used for most moths and butterflies. Purchase them from biological supply houses.

16

LABELS should be placed on the pin of each specimen. They should tell at least where, when, and by whom the specimen was taken. Labels should be neat and small. When much collecting is done at one place, labels printed in advance are useful. These can be ordered from a biological supply house. Sheets of typewritten labels can be photographically reduced to make very small but readable labels.

The species label, containing the scientific name of the specimen, is larger and is usually pinned to the bottom of the collection box by the specimen pin. Supplement your collecting data with a notebook of observations and field records. They may prove to be very useful to you.

STORAGE AND DISPLAY BOXES are of several kinds. The Riker mount, a cotton-filled, flat cardboard box with a glass top, is used for display. For storage of pinned specimens the Schmitt box, with cork bottom, glazed paper lining, and tight-fitting lid, is ideal. The amateur can get along with cigar boxes fitted with balsa or corrugated cardboard bottoms. Clear plastic boxes at least two inches deep are also good. All boxes must be treated periodically with "para" or naphtha moth crystals to keep out destructive insect pests. This is especially important in cigar boxes or in improvised or home-made containers.

Riker Mount

Schmitt Box

plastic box

cigar box

17

OTHER STUDIES of Lepidoptera may be as fascinating as collecting. The life histories of many are still unknown, and much remains to be learned about their habits. Anyone watching insects in the field or rearing them indoors may discover new facts about them. Alert camera fans capture new and interesting details on their film. When your curiosity is aroused, try to find answers to your questions. Keep detailed and accurate records of your observations. Check their completeness by accounting for as many answers as possible to *what, where, when, why, how, how many,* and for *how long.* Record the different species of butterflies and moths seen in your locality, on trips in the field, or at regularly tended light and bait traps. Grow flowers that are attractive to butterflies or that are the food plants on which larvae feed.

BOOKS offer the quickest way to extend your knowledge about butterflies and moths. Try the following:

Clark, Austin H., *The Butterflies of the District of Columbia and Vicinity,* U.S. Nat. Mus. Bull. #157, Wash., D.C., 1932

Comstock, John Adams, *Butterflies of California,* published by the author, Los Angeles, Calif., 1927

Ehrlich, Paul R., and Anne H., *How to Know the Butterflies,* Wm. C. Brown Co., Dubuque, Iowa, 1961

Field, William DeWitt, *A Manual of the Butterflies and Skippers of Kansas,* Bull. of the Univ. of Kansas, Dept. of Entomology, No. 12, Lawrence, Kansas, 1938

Holland, William Jacob, *The Butterfly Book,* Doubleday, Page & Co., Garden City, N.Y., 1931

Holland, William Jacob, *The Moth Book,* Doubleday, Doran & Co., Garden City, N.Y., 1908

Klots, A. B., *A Field Guide to the Butterflies of North America* (East of the Great Plains), Houghton Mifflin Co., Boston, 1951

Oman, P. W., and Cushman, A. D., *Collection and Preservation of Insects,* U.S. Dept. of Agric. Misc. Pub. #601, 1946

Puckering, D. Lovell, and Post, R. L., *Butterflies of North Dakota,* N. Dakota Agric. College, Fargo, N. Dak., 1960

BUTTERFLIES

Butterflies number about 700 species in North America north of Mexico. Recent research shows that some long considered distinct species are merely varieties (sub-species) of others. A few of these are included in this book.

Red-spotted Purple

Butterflies usually fly by day, and rest with their wings erect. Antennae of butterflies are clublike, ending in a swollen tip. Skippers (p. 74) have similar antennae that often turn back in a hook. Antennae of moths are seldom clublike, and are often feathery. Butterflies have a projection (the enlarged humeral lobe) on each hindwing that underlaps the front pair of wings and holds the wings together. Most butterflies pupate as an unprotected chrysalis which hangs freely from a plant or other support. Only a few butterflies are considered destructive, but many moths are pests.

forewing

butterfly antennae

humeral lobe

Pipevine Swallowtail

humeral lobe

hindwing

SWALLOWTAILS are the largest and best known of our butterflies. They are found the world over, mainly in the tropics, and most are brightly colored. There are some two dozen species in North America, most having characteristic tail-like projections from the hindwings, usually one but also two or three in some species. These tails are lacking in the parnassius group (p. 29) and some others. In many species, the females look different from the males in size and markings.

The spherical eggs of swallowtails are laid singly on the food plants, mainly trees and shrubs. Later, the larva may be found resting on a silken mat in a rolled leaf. The swallowtail caterpillar has fleshy horn-like projections of yellow or orange which protrude from behind its head when it is disturbed. Scent glands on these horns give out a strong, disagreeable odor.

When a full-grown swallowtail caterpillar has selected a place to form its chrysalis, it fastens its hindmost feet securely with silk and loops a tough silk thread behind its body, fastening the ends to the support as a kind of "safety belt." Soon the caterpillar sheds its skin, becoming a rough, angular chrysalis, and usually spends the winter in this form. Adults are often seen at flowers and are attracted to wet soil, puddles, or ponds.

PIPEVINE SWALLOWTAIL
larva or caterpillar feeding on pipevine. Chrysalis to the right.

larva

pupa

Pipevine

Polydamas

PIPEVINE SWALLOWTAIL, also called the Blue or Green Swallowtail, is more common in the southern part of its range. The female has slightly larger whitish spots along the margin of the front wings. It lays orange eggs singly on pipevine, snakeroot and knotweed, on which the larva feeds.

3.0-4.5"

3.0-4.0"

POLYDAMAS SWALLOWTAIL is our only tailless black species. The caterpillar and chrysalis are similar to those of the Pipevine Swallowtail, but the caterpillar has reddish tentacles. It also feeds on pipevine. Note the greenish tint to the hindwings.

21

Black Swallowtail
2.8-3.5"

male

female

BLACK SWALLOWTAIL, also called the Common Eastern, or Parsnip, Swallowtail, has variable markings. Some males have hardly any blue on the hindwing. The spots may be larger or may be orange instead of yellow. Occasionally the two rows of spots on the forewing are fused into large triangular areas, or the spots may be greatly reduced. The hindwing in some forms is almost entirely yellow, tinged with orange.

The Black Swallowtail is found in open fields and woodland meadows. It frequents clover and flower gardens, always flying near the ground. The yellowish, ovoid eggs are laid on wild and cultivated plants of the carrot family, such as parsley, parsnip, celery, and carrot. When small, the larva, like that of most swallowtails, is dark brown with a white saddle mark. It becomes green, as illustrated, as it matures. There are two broods of Black Swallowtails annually in the North and at least three in the South.

BAIRD'S SWALLOWTAIL is very closely related to the Black Swallowtail and is also called the Western Black Swallowtail. The males are similar, but there is some difference in the females, which have less yellow than the eastern species. This butterfly is variable; some are quite yellow, some almost entirely black. The caterpillar feeds on sagebrush (Artemesia), and not on plants of the carrot family. There is one brood annually.

ANISE SWALLOWTAIL is probably the most common swallowtail west of the Rocky Mountains. The early stages of the larva closely resemble those of the Black Swallowtail in form and color. The larva feeds mainly on anise or Sweet Fennel of the carrot family. The adult female looks very much like the male.

22

Baird's Swallowtail
3.3-3.5"
female

Anise Swallowtail
2.5-3.5"

Black Swallowtail

pupa

larva

hindwings

Black
2.8-3.5"

Indra
2.0-3.0"

INDRA, or Mountain Swallowtail, can be distinguished from Baird's and Black by its short tail. Its light wing band is variable in size. Another species, the Short-tailed Swallowtail, occurs in eastern Canada. 2.0-3.0"

Anise

Baird's

Black

4.5-5.5"

PALAMEDES SWALLOW-TAIL, common in the South, approaches the Giant (p. 25) in size. It prefers the margins of swampy woods, where in slow flight it sometimes rises to tall treetops. The eggs are laid on the food plants—bay, magnolia, and Sassafras. The caterpillar resembles the Spicebush (p. 26), but the reddish spot on the third body segment is not so distinct and lacks the black ring. Pala-

medes Swallowtails have two to three broods annually.

ALASKAN SWALLOWTAIL is a smaller and more yellow northern variety of the European, or Old World, Swallowtail that is common in Europe and Asia. Another variety of this Old World species is found near Hudson Bay in Canada. The caterpillar resembles that of the Black Swallowtail (p. 22) and also feeds on plants of the carrot family.

Alaskan Swallowtail
2.8-3.0"

4.0-5.5"

GIANT SWALLOWTAIL caterpillars are known as Orange Dogs or Orange Puppies in the South, where they do occasional damage to citrus trees, especially in young groves. Four or five hundred eggs may be laid by one female, deposited one at a time near tips of leaves or branches. The caterpillars feed on Prickly Ash and the Hop Tree in addition to citrus.

The Giant Swallowtail is more common in the southern part of its range, where it is likely to have three instead of two broods. First-brood adults emerge from chrysalids in May. The Giant Swallowtail has a leisurely flight, sometimes sailing with outstretched wings, which then show the bright yellow underside in contrast to the brown upperside. The Giant frequents open fields and gardens, sipping nectar from flowers and moisture from mud.

larva

4.0-5.0"

Hindwing of female is blue instead of greenish.

SPICEBUSH SWALLOWTAIL

is sometimes called the Green-clouded Swallowtail because the male's hindwing has a pronounced greenish tone. This species has a red-orange spot on the upper margin of the hindwing above.

These swallowtails frequent low, damp woods, visiting open fields less often than many other swallowtails. They are active, steady fliers and seldom alight. Numbers of them often gather at puddles on woodland roads or at other wet places. This butterfly has several geographic forms, some with larger yellow spots and other variations.

There are two broods in the North, three in the South. Butterflies of the first brood, which emerge from chrysalids in late April or early May, after spending the winter in the pupal stage, are smaller than those which emerge from later broods in the summer.

The larva feeds on Spicebush, Sassafras, Sweet Bay, and Prickly Ash. Like other swallowtail caterpillars it forms a mat of silk on the upper surface of a leaf; then it draws the leaf together and hides when not feeding. As it grows the larva constructs new and larger shelters until it is ready to pupate.

larva

Eastern Tiger Swallowtail
4.0-5.5"

male

female
light phase

larva

female
dark phase

**EASTERN TIGER SWAL-
LOWTAIL** shows difference in
color between sexes. Females are
dimorphic (show two color
forms); some are yellow and others dark brown. The dark form
is uncommon in the North. The
larva of the Eastern Tiger Swallowtail feeds mostly on Wild
Cherry and Tuliptrees.

**WESTERN TIGER SWAL-
LOWTAIL** is not dimorphic. It
differs from the Eastern Swallowtail in having the spots on the
underside of the forewing merge
to form a band (see below). The
caterpillar is like that of the Eastern Tiger Swallowtail but feeds
on willow, poplar, and hops,
plants of moist western areas.

Underside of forewing:

Eastern Tiger
spotted

Western Tiger
banded

27

4.0-6.0"

TWO-TAILED SWALLOW-TAIL, our largest butterfly, occurs from British Columbia to Calif. and eastward to western Texas and Montana. The cater-pillar feeds on cherry, hoptree, ash, privet, and shadbush. Probably breeds twice each year. The smaller Three-tailed Swallowtail occurs in Arizona and Mexico.

PALE SWALLOWTAIL occurs all along the West Coast to the eastern slope of the Rockies and is quite common locally. Larva feeds chiefly on buckthorn. At least two broods occur annually.

ZEBRA SWALLOWTAIL, an eastern species more common in the South, varies in marking and size. Spring forms are smallest; later broods larger with longer tails. Larva feeds on pawpaw.

3.8-4.5"

3.5-4.0"

larva

PARNASSIUS is a more primitive genus than *Papilio*, the true swallowtails. The larva shows many habits of skippers (pp. 74-80) and, like them, is covered with short hairs. It lacks the scent horns of swallowtails. The pupa is not like those of swallowtails either, but, like those of skippers, is smooth and brownish, and is formed in a leafy shelter on the ground or in grass. The adult parnassius is not like swallowtails in shape or coloration but is pale white or yellowish, with markings that vary greatly. Parnassians occur mostly in the mountains, where adults are on the wing by midsummer. Female bodies lack the hairiness of the male.

CLODIUS, a variable species, is distinguished from Smintheus by its black antennae. It lacks the red spots on the forewings which Smintheus often has.

SMINTHEUS differs from our other parnassians in having white antennae with black rings. The larva feeds on stonecrop (*Sedum*) and saxifrage (*Saxifraga*).

Smintheus larva

Smintheus
2.5-3.0"

Clodius
2.5-3.0"

SULPHURS AND WHITES form a world-wide family of several hundred species, including many species in temperate parts of the Northern Hemisphere. They are among the first butterflies to appear in spring. Nearly all are yellow, orange, or white. Females differ from males in pattern and often in color. The butter-yellow color of European sulphurs probably suggested the name *butterfly*. Some are often seen around the edges of puddles. Eggs are spindle-shaped, sculptured with fine ridges and pits. The larva, usually long, green, and slender with little hair, feeds mainly on legumes and mustards. Some are crop pests. The pupa, often compressed and triangular, is held in place by a silk girdle. Most species have more than one brood a year, especially in the South, where three or even more may occur.

ALFALFA BUTTERFLY, also called the Orange Sulphur, occurs in many hybrid forms, crossing with the Clouded Sulphur. It can be distinguished from the Clouded Sulphur by the orange of the uppersides. The undersides of both are similar. Some females are white. The larva is a pest of alfalfa. Several broods each year. The butterfly ranges from Canada to Mexico.

male
1.8-2.0"

female

female

male
1.3-2.3"

white female

larva

pupa

CLOUDED SULPHUR, also called the Common Sulphur, ranges through most of North America but is most common in the East. It is the "puddle butterfly" which swarms in moist places and over clover fields. Some females are white like the Alfalfa Butterfly, but generally the Clouded Sulphur has less black on the margin of the wings. The larva is more common on clover than on alfalfa and cannot be told from that of the Alfalfa Butterfly. There are several broods yearly.

PINK-EDGED SULPHUR can be distinguished from other sulphurs by the pink wing edges and the pink-edged silver spot on the underside of each hindwing.

▼

1.3-2.0"

Clouded

Alfalfa

male
Sara Orange Tip
1.0-1.3"
female

SARA ORANGE TIP is variable. The underside of the hindwings has an irregular "mossy" appearance from the greenish marbling. The amount of marbling is reduced in the second of the two annual generations. Larva feeds on wild mustards.

OLYMPIAN MARBLE, named for the pronounced green marbling on the underside of the hindwing, is closely related to the orange tips. The larva feeds mostly on Hedge Mustard. The Olympian Marble produces only one brood a year, in the spring.

Falcate Orange Tip
1.6-1.7"

male

female

1.3-1.5"

larva

FALCATE ORANGE TIP is among the first butterflies to emerge in spring. It frequents open damp woods, flying near the ground. It is named for the sickle-shaped apex of the forewing. The larva feeds on plants of the mustard family.

male
2.8-3.3"

female

ORANGE-BARRED SULPHUR is common along the Gulf of Mexico, occasionally straying into middle Atlantic and midwestern states. The larva, yellowish-green, with black and yellow bands and small black spines, feeds on Cassia and on other closely related plants of the pea family. At least two broods each year.

CLOUDLESS SULPHUR, also known as the Giant Sulphur, is abundant in the tropics and common in our southern states. Huge flocks during migration are an impressive sight. Breeding is continuous in the tropics, but to the north there are two broods with adults overwintering. Wild Senna is its chief food.

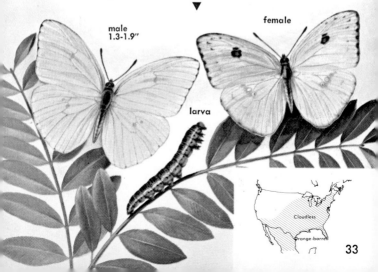

male
1.3-1.9"

female

larva

Cloudless

Orange-barred

33

male
1.8-2.0"

female

▲

CALIFORNIA DOG-FACE can be separated from the Southern Dog-face by the lack of dark margins on the upperside of the hindwing. It sometimes strays eastward from its normal range.

The larva feeds on False Indigo. Two broods develop yearly; the adults are on the wing in spring and midsummer. The name dog-face comes from the "poodle face" marking on the forewing.

SOUTHERN DOG-FACE noted for its rapid flight, is more common in the southern part of its range. Like the California Dog-face, it is double-brooded. The larva, highly variable in markings, feeds on Wild Indigo and also on various clovers.

2.3-2.5"

◄

1.3-1.6"

larva

Little Sulphur

pupa

▲

LITTLE SULPHUR is common east of the Rockies. The larva feeds on Senna, Partridge Pea, and other legumes. There are two or three broods a year. This species migrates in large flocks.

34

1.5-2.0"

Sleepy Sulphur underside

SLEEPY SULPHUR is so named because it is slower in flight than other sulphurs. It is very common in the South, where it breeds throughout most of the year. Males frequently congregate in large numbers at puddles. The velvety green larva with a yellowish stripe on each side feeds mainly on Senna.

1.0-1.3"

FAIRY YELLOW, also known as Barred Sulphur, has a gray bar in the forewing of males and some females. It ranges from Florida and Texas southward, feeding on Joint Vetch and other legumes.

0.8-1.3"

DAINTY DWARF occurs from Ga. to southern Calif. and up the Miss. Valley to the Great Lakes. Females are heavily marked with black. It is double-brooded.

1.3-1.6"

MUSTARD WHITE has a circumpolar range. The veins on the underside are outlined with dark scales. The larva, green with greenish-yellow stripes, feeds on various mustards.

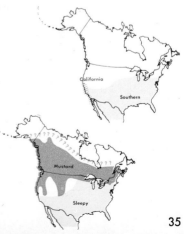

California

Southern

Mustard

Sleepy

35

1.5-2.0"   1.8-2.3"

PINE WHITE, a pest of pines and Balsam Fir in the West, has one brood and overwinters as eggs. The female has more black markings than the male.

GIANT WHITE is common in the tropics and breeds to southern Texas, straying northward. Like the Great Southern White it also has a dark phase.

GREAT SOUTHERN WHITE of the Gulf Coast and Miss. Valley, sometimes migrates. If so, a dark phase is involved. The larva feeds mostly on mustards.

FLORIDA WHITE is a widespread butterfly that strays north from Fla. and Tex. All have orange on the undersides; most females also have dark marks.

2.5-2.8"   1.6-2.3"

female and larva

male
1.3-1.6"

CHECKERED WHITE, or Common White, occurs all over temperate N.A. It was more common before the Cabbage Butterfly arrived and spread. Larva feeds on cabbage and other mustards. Adults occur early in spring and produce at least three broods.

CABBAGE BUTTERFLY, since its introduction a century ago, has spread across N.A. to become a crop pest. Besides cabbage, the larva feeds on other mustards, also on nasturtium. It is one of the first butterflies to emerge in spring.

larva

female

male
1.3-1.8"

Cabbage

Checkered

MILKWEED BUTTERFLIES form a chiefly tropical family with only two species common in North America. They are reputed to have disagreeable tastes and odors which seem to make birds avoid eating them.

3.5-3.9"

THE MONARCH, one of the best known butterflies, is noted for its migrations. In the fall, flocks of Monarchs move southward to Texas, California, and Florida. Resting flocks of fall migrants or winter residents may cover entire trees. In spring they straggle northward, producing broods along the way. Some travel as far as southern Canada. Three or four broods may be produced in one year. Females lack the spot of dark scales in the center of the hindwings that marks the male scent glands. Females differ also in having broader black vein lines. The larva feeds on milkweeds, Dogbane, and related plants. This may be the source of its reputed bad taste. About one month is required for its life history, from the conical egg laid singly on leaves or blossoms to the adult, which emerges from the shiny green, gold-speckled, hanging chrysalis. The larva, striped with yellow, black, and white, is about 2 in. long when fully grown.

3.1-3.3"

THE QUEEN resembles the Monarch but is smaller and darker brown. The brownish larva with brown and yellow transverse stripes feeds on milkweeds. There are three broods a year. A sub-species called a Bates' Queen has the veins of the upperside of the hindwing narrowly edged with grayish white. It occurs in southern Arizona, New Mexico, and Texas.

Monarch pupa

larva

THE SATYRS are butterflies of rather dull color, usually brown or gray, often with eyespots on both upper and under sides. The forewing veins are generally swollen at the base. Most prefer woods or woods margins. When alarmed they may hide in the grass. The satyr larva tapers from the middle toward each end and has a forked tail. It feeds at night, chiefly on grasses. The pupa usually hangs freely from the posterior end. Growth is slow, usually with only one brood annually. Satyrs overwinter as larvae.

EYED BROWN has a weak dancing flight. It frequents damp meadows with tall grasses and also woods margins. Local colonies are found east of the Rockies from Canada to the Carolinas.

pupa

larva

1.8-2.0"

1.6-2.0"

1.6-2.0"

◀ **CREOLE PEARLY EYE** is found locally in the Midwest and Southeast. Streaks of raised dark scales mark the male forewing. The female's forewing has five eyespots underneath.

◀ **PEARLY EYE** occurs locally in the East. Male differs from Creole in lacking raised dark scales on forewing. Female's forewing usually has 4 eyespots below.

40

Little Wood
1.8-2.0"

underside

Gemmed
1.8"

Carolina
1.5"

Georgia
1.7"

LITTLE WOOD SATYR prefers open woods and meadows overgrown with shrubbery. Occurs east of the Rockies.

CAROLINA SATYR is mousegray above, without eyespots. Occurs from N.J. to Fla., west to Texas, and up the Miss. Valley.

GEMMED SATYR is marked by a prominent violet-gray patch under its hindwing. Virginia to Illinois, south to Fla. and Mex.

GEORGIA SATYR prefers marshy areas or open pine woods. Distribution is similar to that of the Carolina Satyr.

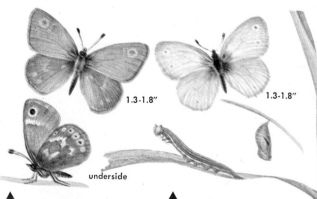

1.3-1.8"

1.3-1.8"

underside

▲
PLAIN RINGLET ranges through Canada and down into the northern Midwest. The underside of its hindwing has an isolated light-colored patch.

▲
CALIFORNIA RINGLET is very common west of the Rockies. It is near-white above, darker below, with an angular white patch on its hindwing.

41

RIDING'S SATYR at rest is the color of mossy rock and thus is well camouflaged in its environment. Pupa forms underground.

COMMON ALPINE is common in spring in the mountains from New Mexico to Wash. and Alaska. Larva feeds on grasses.

COMMON WOOD NYMPH varies so in color and pattern in its nation-wide range that different forms are hard to recognize. The northeastern form is illustrated. Southeastern form is larger, and the lower eyespot on the forewing is smaller. In the West it is darker and smaller, and does not have the light band on the forewing.

NEVADA ARCTIC is also called the Greater Arctic. The female lacks the dark shading on the male's forewing. Other species of arctics, mostly smaller and some without eyespots, occur in Canada, the Rockies, and alpine New England.

1.5-1.8"

1.8"

2.0-2.8"

Common Wood Nymph   larva

pupa

Riding's

2.3-2.5"

THE HELICONIANS are peculiar to the American tropics. They are reputed to be protected against predators by their unsavory taste and odor. Some are mimicked by other species and even by other heliconians. The forewings are twice as long as wide, the forelegs tiny and useless, and the head large. The eggs are rounded, about twice as long as wide. Larva feeds on Passion Flower leaves; pupa is unusually angular.

2.6-2.8"

GULF FRITILLARY is neither a true heliconian nor a true fritillary (p. 44). It ranges through South America to New Jersey and Iowa.

JULIA, found in southern Fla. and southern Texas, is a South and Central American species which occasionally appears in large swarms in southern Florida or Texas. It is a strong flier. The female is much lighter and duller than the male.

3.2-3.8"

ZEBRAS, found in woods or near wood borders, gather in colonies at night. They are weak fliers and move about slowly. Males are attracted to chrysalids of females just before the latter emerge. Strays from tropical Amer. to S.C. and Kansas.

larva

pupa

3.0-3.4"

BRUSH-FOOTED BUTTERFLIES are named for their tiny forelegs, hairy and useless for walking. Next to skippers they make up the largest butterfly family. Most are medium- to large-sized species.

THE GREATER FRITILLARIES are common in temperate regions. Males and females sometimes differ in color and markings. Caterpillars feed at night, mostly on violets. They remain hidden during the day. Most fritillaries raise a single brood and overwinter as larvae.

VARIEGATED FRITILLARY ranges over most of the U.S. except the Pacific Northwest. It lacks the typical silver spots on the underside of the wings. The Mexican Fritillary, similar in form but with plainer hindwings, is found from southern Texas to southern California.

REGAL FRITILLARY frequents roadsides and wet meadows, feeding on milkweed and thistle. Both rows of spots on the hindwing are creamy white on the female but only the inner row is on the male. Larva is like Great Spangled's but black, mottled with yellow.

Variegated
Fritillary
2.3-2.5"

Regal Fritillary
3.4-3.6"

pupa

larva

pupa

underside

GREAT SPANGLED FRITIL-LARY is single-brooded in the North and double-brooded in the South. Larva hibernates soon after hatching and the following spring feeds at night on violets. The adults, in typical fritillary fashion, prefer marshes and damp meadows. This is one of the best known fritillaries.

3.3-3.8"

APHRODITE FRITILLARY, similar to Great Spangled, is smaller and has a narrow, yellow marginal band under the hindwing. It prefers high eleva-tions. Another species, the Mountain, resembles Aphrodite, but the hindwing beneath is darker and forewing has a dark margin. From so. Can. to the Rockies.

Great Spangled

Regal

3.0-3.3"

45

female

male
3.7-3.8"

▲
DIANA is an unusual fritillary because the sexes differ so in color and markings and because it prefers woodlands to open country and is more attracted to manure piles than to flowers. It ranges from the southern Appalachian Mts. west to Illinois.

NEVADA FRITILLARY is quite common in sections of the Rockies and foothills of the Sierra Nevadas. Greenish underside of hindwing is a good identifying characteristic.

EURYNOME resembles the Nevada Fritillary, but the greenish tint covers only top third of underside of the hindwing. Occurs in the Rockies from N. Mex. to Can., west to Cascades.

▼

▼

2.5-3.5"

1.7-2.0"

LESSER FRITILLARIES resemble greater fritillaries but are smaller, and most lack the silver spots under the hindwing. Several species occur in the Arctic; none range far South. Larvae resemble those of the greater fritillaries but do not hibernate as soon after hatching. They also feed on violets but are known to eat other plants as well.

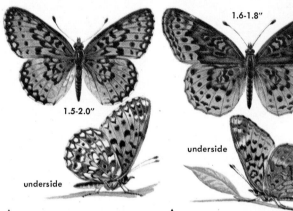

1.6-1.8"

underside

1.5-2.0"

underside

▲
SILVER-BORDERED FRITIL-LARY appears in many varieties. Some are also found in Europe. All have the heavily silvered underside of the hindwing.

▲
EASTERN MEADOW FRITIL-LARY has outer margin angled near apex, not curved as in other fritillaries. It lacks the dark outer margin, but has black spots.

1.5-1.9"

underside

◄ **WESTERN MEADOW FRITIL-LARY** resembles the Silver-bordered in shape but is different beneath. Those in the North are darker above than those in the South. They are common in mountain valleys of the West, ranging from Colorado to California and north to British Columbia.

47

THE CHECKERSPOTS, small- to medium-sized, lay their eggs in groups. The spiny caterpillars feed together for a while. The free-hanging pupa is whitish with dark blotches.

1.8-2.6"

(1) THE BALTIMORE, though widespread, is local, seldom found far from its wet meadow food plant, Turtlehead. Many variations occur. Several species are found in the West.

(1)

larva

(2)
1.5-1.6"

pupa

(2) SILVERY CHECKERSPOT is similar to Harris' on the upper surface. Found along roads, lakes, and open meadows from Maine to North Carolina and west to the Rockies.

(3)
1.4-1.7"

(3) HARRIS' CHECKERSPOT is also variable and very local. It prefers damp fields and underbrush. Ranges from Nova Scotia west to Manitoba and south to Illinois and W. Va.

(3) underside

(4)

(4) CHALCEDON CHECKERSPOT is quite variable in color and pattern. It is common along the Pacific in the lower mountain levels and feeds on plants of the figwort family.

1.8-3.0"

Chalcedon

Baltimore

48

THE CRESCENTS are closely allied to checkerspots but are smaller. Named for pale crescent on outer margin of the hindwing, beneath. The larvae stay together but do not make webs. Summer brood is paler than the winter brood.

(1) MYLITTA CRESCENT, abundant on the West Coast, varies greatly. It generally shows a pale crescent both above and beneath. Larva feeds on thistles.

(2) FIELD CRESCENT is common in California and occurs from Arizona to Alaska, with both spring and fall broods, in damp meadows and along streams. Larva feeds on asters.

(3) PHAON CRESCENT is easy to tell from other crescents by its underside. The forewing above has a band of white to yellowish spots. Gulf states to Calif.

(4) PEARL CRESCENT, one of the most common butterflies, is found around puddles and flowers. It ranges over all North America south of Hudson Bay, except for the Pacific Coast.

underside

(1)

1.2-1.5"

(2)
1.2-1.4"

(3)
0.9-1.3"

(4)
1.3-1.7"

light female

(4)

dark female

larva

pupa

(4)

ANGLE WINGS are named for the sharp, angular margins of their wings. The undersides of the wings closely resemble dead leaves or bark, camouflaging angle wings in their woodland haunts. Eggs sometimes occur in a hanging chain. The larva is spiny; the angular pupa hangs free. Like crescents, angle wings have light and dark seasonal forms. They hibernate as adults.

2.5-2.8"

larva

pupa

QUESTION MARK, the largest angle wing, is named for the silvery mark on the underside of its hindwing. The purplish margin of the wings is also distinctive. The larva feeds mainly on elm.

SATYR lacks the broad, dark hindwing margin of Comma. Unlike the Zephyr, it is brown beneath, and lacks the greenish luster above of the Fawn. Larva feeds mostly in nettles.

underside

1.8-2.0"

Satyr

Question Mark

Comma larva

Comma pupa

1.8-2.0"

hindwing of dark form

underside

Zephr 1.8-2.0"

COMMA is a common angle wing of moist open woodland. Larva feeds on nettle and hops. As in all angle wings, the Comma has a dark summer form, shown in the hindwing detail.

2.0-2.2"

FAWN, or Green Comma, has a greenish tint to its wings. Found in the mountains from eastern Canada and Carolinas to the N.W. states. Larva lives on birch and alder, feeding on the undersides of leaves.

ZEPHYR, like the Satyr, lacks dark margin on hindwing but is gray beneath. Seen from May to Sept. Larva feeds on elm and currant. The darker form below was once considered a separate species—*silenus.*

▼ dark form

51

BUCKEYES are brightly colored butterflies, all of which have a large eyespot on the upperside of both the hind and the fore wings. There are over one hundred species throughout the world, but only one of them is common in North America.

(1)

2.0-2.3"

underside

(7)

(2)

(6)

(3)

(4)

(5)

Buckeye

Painted Lady

THE BUCKEYE, a variable species, overwinters as an adult. Larva feeds mainly on plantain and Gerardia. In its development, larva (1) attaches itself to a support (2) and becomes a pupa (3). Adult develops in the pupa (4) and emerges with soft wings (5) which soon expand (6) and dry (7).

THISTLE BUTTERFLIES are a widespread group. One species, the Painted Lady, ranges through all temperate and some tropical areas. These butterflies frequent flowers, especially thistles. Adults hibernate. Some species migrate. The larvae are spiny.

Painted Lady
2.0-2.3"

underside

West Coast Lady
2.0-2.3"

underside

PAINTED LADY is called the Cosmopolitan because of its wide range. It is also noted for its migrations. The larva builds a webbed nest on the food plant, usually thistle. Adults prefer open places. There are usually two broods a year in the North.

WEST COAST LADY ranges from the Rockies westward and south to Argentina. It differs from the Painted Lady in lacking the white bar on the upper surface of the forewing. It is easily captured while feeding on flowers. The larva feeds on mallows.

2.0-2.3"

underside

pupa

larva

▲
RED ADMIRAL is found world-wide in north temperate regions. It is a swift erratic flier seen in open woodland and around Butterfly Bush. The larva lives and feeds singly on leaves of nettles, the edges of which it draws together with silk. Adults hibernate. The Red Admiral is double-brooded; the second brood is larger and darker than one shown here. The ranges of the Red Admiral and American Painted Lady are almost alike.

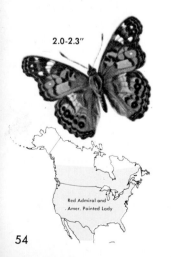

2.0-2.3"

Red Admiral and Amer. Painted Lady

underside

AMERICAN PAINTED LADY, or Hunter's Butterfly, has two large eyespots on the underside of the hindwing. Painted and West Coast Ladies have 5 small spots each. Greenish eggs are laid on everlasting and burdock. Larva is black with yellow stripes.

TORTOISE SHELLS include butterflies that resemble angle wings, but the inner margin of the forewing is straight instead of concave. Adults hibernate and may be seen very early in spring. Eggs are laid in clusters. Tortoise shells are a circumpolar group which is widespread in the Northern Hemisphere.

COMPTON TORTOISE SHELL frequents open woodlands, where its undersides provide excellent camouflage.

MILBERT'S TORTOISE SHELL is a northern species of open areas and mountain meadows. Larva feeds on nettle.

MOURNING CLOAK occurs throughout temperate N.A. Adults that have hibernated may be seen sunning in early spring with open wings. Eggs are laid in masses around the twigs of elm, willow and poplar. Larvae may become pests.

Mourning Cloak larva

Compton Tortoise Shell
2.6-2.8"

Milbert's Tortoise Shell

1.8"

pupa

Mourning Cloak

2.8-3.3"

Compton

Milbert's

ADMIRALS AND SISTERS total six species in N.A. The larva, not as spiny as those of other brush-footed butterflies, feeds on a variety of trees. These species are mostly double-brooded, and the tiny larva hibernates in silken shelters on the food plant.

WHITE ADMIRAL, or Banded Purple, lives in upland hardwood forests and on mountain slopes, where its larva feeds mostly on birch, willow, and poplar. The adult is readily attracted by putrid barnyard odors.

Viceroy
young larva
hibernating

resting

3.1-3.4"

full grown

2.6-2.8"

pupa

VICEROY, red-brown in color, mimics the reputedly distasteful Monarch Butterfly (p. 38). It is found in open places, where the larva feeds on willow and poplar. Larva hibernates and develops as shown above.

White

Viceroy

WEIDEMEYER'S ADMIRAL has white spots along the margin of the forewing. Found on mountain slopes and wet places where aspen and willow grow.

LORQUIN'S ADMIRAL has an orange tip to forewing and a white band on both wings. Found in river bottomland. Larva feeds on cherry, willow, and poplar.

3.0-3.3"

2.3-2.8"

3.1-3.4"

RED-SPOTTED PURPLE, considered by some to be a subspecies of the White Admiral, prefers lower altitudes and a warmer climate than that species. It also prefers more open areas, where the larva feeds mostly on Wild Cherry.

Lorquin's

Weidemeyer's Red-spotted

2.5-3.0"

CALIFORNIA SISTER is similar to Lorquin's Admiral but has blue lines on undersides of wings. It is a common California butterfly, frequenting the upper branches of live oaks, on which the larva feeds. The butterfly rarely sips nectar from flowers.

LEAFWING BUTTERFLIES are a tropical group in which the undersides of the wings resemble a dead leaf. Color and wing shape vary greatly. Two seasonal forms occur—a wet and a dry. The forewings of the latter are less curved. Larva hides by day in a rolled leaf. The goatweed butterflies are our only examples.

1.9-2.2"

1.9-2.2"

GOATWEED BUTTERFLY ranges from Ga. and Tex. up the Miss. Valley. Its dry-season form is lighter in color. Female is like Morrison's, but light spots on wings form a continuous band.

MORRISON'S GOATWEED has a tropical range but enters Texas. Male is quite similar to Goatweed Butterfly but is more brilliant. Female (illustrated) differs in color and pattern.

58

EMPEROR, OR HACKBERRY, BUTTERFLIES are found near Hackberry trees, on which the larva feeds in colonies. The striped caterpillar tapers toward both ends and bears two "horns" behind the head. It hibernates when partly grown. Adults show much geographic variation. The females are larger than the males and are also lighter in color.

Hackberry larvae and pupa

Hackberry female
1.9-2.4"

Tawny Emperor
1.9-2.6"

Towny

Hackberry

HACKBERRY BUTTERFLY ranges widely in open woodlands. Individuals often have a choice perch on which they repeatedly land. Some varieties of this butterfly have an incomplete eyespot, or one or two dark eyespots in addition to the typical spot on the forewing. Some are much lighter than normal.

TAWNY EMPEROR is more common in the South, though it ranges north to New England. Lacks dark eyespots on the forewing. Larva similar to Hackberry Butterfly's but has branched head spines.

Florida Purple Wing 1.6-2.0"

2.6-2.8"

Ruddy Dagger Wing

PURPLE WINGS are tropical butterflies, usually dull purplish above and well marked on the undersides. Two species occur in southern Florida and Texas.

DAGGER WINGS are mainly tropical butterflies, with prolonged tips to their forewings, resembling small swallowtails. One species breeds in the United States.

FLORIDA PURPLE WING occurs in dense hardwood hammocks. Dingy Purple Wing (not shown) is slightly smaller and lacks most of the purple sheen.

RUDDY DAGGER WING of southern Fla. and Texas, may stray northward. The ornate filament-bearing larva feeds on fig and *Anacardium*.

TROPIC QUEENS are tropical butterflies noted for their beauty and the females' trait of mimicking milkweed butterflies (p. 38). The Mimic is a species that was probably introduced into the American tropics from the Old World a long time ago. It occurs in the West Indies and locally in Florida.

Mimic male 2.5-3.0"

Mimic female

METALMARKS are small butterflies usually having metallic spots, from which the common name is derived. Many of the fifteen plainly colored species occurring north of Mexico are difficult to distinguish. In the tropics, metalmarks are common and occur in many different bright color patterns. Males have four walking legs, females six. They rest with wings outstretched. The larva resembles those of hairstreaks. The pupa is hairy, suspended by a stem, and supported by a silk thread.

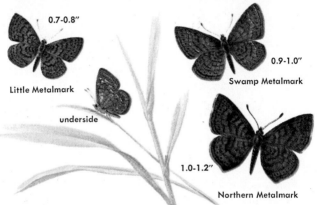

0.7-0.8"

Little Metalmark

underside

0.9-1.0"

Swamp Metalmark

1.0-1.2"

Northern Metalmark

LITTLE METALMARK is more common in the southern part of its range. It occurs in open grassy areas, where it is distinguished by its small size and its uncheckered wing margins.

NORTHERN METALMARK is relatively rare but has been confused with similar, more common species. It prefers dry hilly terrain and open woods. Wings have an irregular dark band and also have checkered light and dark margins.

SWAMP METALMARK lacks dark band; wing margins are lightly checkered. Occurs in wet meadows and swamps in summer. Overwinters as larva, which feeds on Swamp Thistle.

Swamp
Northern
Little

61

dark male

1.1"

light male

underside

1.0-1.3"

MORMON METALMARK, a desert species, occurs through the Southwest. Its wing spots are white rather than metallic. Amounts of gray or brown on hindwing vary as shown.

NAIS METALMARK occurs from Colorado to Mexico. Its wing fringes are checkered, but in overall appearance it is not distinctly like other metalmarks. The larva feeds on Wild Plum.

SNOUT BUTTERFLIES are easily recognized by their long projecting mouth parts (palpi) which resemble snouts. Like the metalmarks, males have four walking legs and the females six. The Common Snout Butterfly is the only snout butterfly regularly occurring north of Mexico. The larva, which grows very rapidly, feeds on Hackberry.

underside

larva

Snout

Common Snout Butterfly
1.8-2.0"

HAIRSTREAKS are small- to medium-sized butterflies, usually with hair-like tails on the hindwings. The "streak" part of the common name comes from narrow bands on the undersides of the wings. Hairstreaks have a swift, darting flight and are readily attracted to flowers. There are about 65 species north of Mexico.

underside

larva

male
1.4"

1.1"

female, underside

GRAY or COMMON HAIR-STREAK is also called the Cotton Square Borer or the Bean Lycaenid because of damage it sometimes does to crops. It overwinters in the pupal stage and emerges early in the spring.

GREAT PURPLE HAIR-STREAK has two tails on each hindwing, especially pronounced on the female. The female lacks sex-pads—black spots on forewing. The larva feeds on mistletoe. Double-brooded.

◄ **COLORADO HAIRSTREAK** is actually more purple in color than the Great Purple. The underside has a typical banded pattern. This species is commonly found around scrub oaks.

1.5"

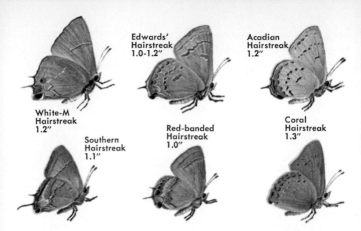

Edwards' Hairstreak 1.0-1.2"

Acadian Hairstreak 1.2"

White-M Hairstreak 1.2"

Southern Hairstreak 1.1"

Red-banded Hairstreak 1.0"

Coral Hairstreak 1.3"

WHITE-M HAIRSTREAK, a southeastern species, is named for the inverted white M mark in the inner band on the underside of hindwing. Upper surface blue.

ACADIAN HAIRSTREAK has widely separated spots instead of transverse lines. The larva feeds on willow. Adults are found in wet areas where willows grow.

RED-BANDED HAIRSTREAK occurs from Fla. to N.Y. and from Mexico to Mich. It is most common in the South. Upperside is brownish black.

EDWARDS' HAIRSTREAK has oval spots that make broken transverse lines. It frequents thickets of Scrub Oak, on which the larva feeds.

SOUTHERN HAIRSTREAK has orange patches on the upperside of both wings, larger on the hindwing. It is single-brooded. The larva feeds on oak.

CORAL HAIRSTREAK is tailless. Coral red spots on underside may form a solid band. It overwinters in the egg stage. Adults appear by midsummer.

California
Hairstreak
1.1-1.3"

Banded
Hairstreak
1.0-1.2"

Hedgerow
Hairstreak
1.2"

Striped
Hairstreak
1.2"

Olive
Hairstreak
0.9-1.0"

Sylvan
Hairstreak
1.0"

CALIFORNIA HAIRSTREAK is single-brooded, appearing on the wing in midsummer in the foothills. Larva feeds on *Ceanothus* and, probably, on oak.

HEDGEROW HAIRSTREAK, reddish brown above, is common in the Rockies and west to the Pacific coast in summer. Feeds on *Cercocarpus* and *Ceanothus*.

OLIVE HAIRSTREAK, double-brooded, overwinters as a pupa. The adults occur in spring and midsummer, usually near red cedars, the larval food plants.

BANDED HAIRSTREAK occurs in late spring and early summer, usually in or near woodlands. It overwinters in the egg stage. The larva feeds on oak and hickory.

STRIPED HAIRSTREAK is distinctly striped underneath. It is widely distributed east of the Rockies. The larva feeds on many plants, including oak and willow.

SYLVAN HAIRSTREAK resembles California Hairstreak but is lighter beneath and has only one small red spot. The larva feeds on willow.

Banded Elfin
male
0.8-1.2"

Western Banded Elfin
1.2"
underside

underside

larva

Brown Elfin
0.9-1.0"

Banded Elfin
female

ELFINS are small- to medium-sized brown butterflies; females are somewhat larger and less drab than the males. Elfins overwinter as pupae and have only a single brood each year. They are among the first butterflies to appear in spring.

WESTERN BANDED ELFIN resembles the Banded Elfin, but the band (middle of forewing, underside) is less irregular. Larva feeds on pine.

BANDED ELFIN, also called the Pine Elfin, is usually found along the borders of open pine woods. The larva feeds on the seedlings of the hard pines, such as Virginia Pine and Pitch Pine, on which it is well camouflaged.

BROWN ELFIN, reddish brown on the underside, is found in and along the edges of open woods where its food plants, blueberry and Sheep Laurel, grow.

Western Elfin
·0.9-1.0"

Hoary Elfin
0.9-1.0"

Henry's Elfin
0.9-1.1"

Frosted Elfin
0.9-1.5"

WESTERN ELFIN is obscurely marked beneath. It occurs in both lowlands and mountains, often frequenting *Ceanothus* blossoms. The larva feeds on sedum.

HENRY'S ELFIN of open woods is less gray on the underside and is dark brown at the base of the scalloped hindwing. The larva feeds on blueberry.

HOARY ELFIN gets its name from the gray color on the underside. It occurs in open, dry, heath-covered areas. The larva feeds on bearberry.

FROSTED ELFIN male has a sex-spot on the upperside of forewing. Hindwing has more scalloped border and less color contrast than that of Henry's Elfin.

67

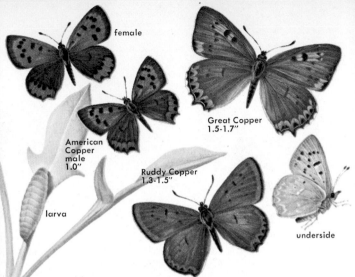

female

Great Copper
1.5-1.7"

American
Copper
male
1.0"

Ruddy Copper
1.3-1.5"

larva

underside

COPPERS occur chiefly in the Northern Hemisphere, with about sixteen species in the United States and Canada. Most are reddish or brown and have a coppery luster, but one, the Blue Copper, is bright blue. Most species frequent open areas and roadsides.

AMERICAN COPPER occurs from spring to fall in fields where Sheep Sorrel, food plant of the larva, grows. Overwinters in the pupal stage. Adults in spring are brighter and less spotted.

GREAT COPPER is one of the largest of the coppers. Males have fewer black dots and less orange on the wing margins. The females feed on dock. Adults emerge in summer.

RUDDY COPPERS have white margins on the wings and are less black-spotted on the underside of the hindwing than other coppers. The female resembles the American Copper but is larger and not as brightly colored. Feeds on Arnica.

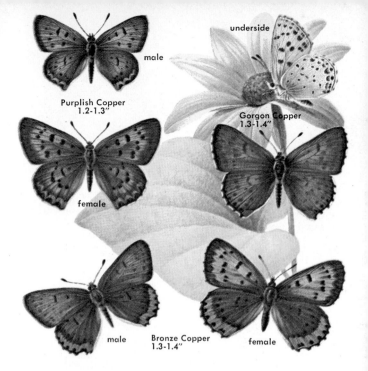

underside

Purplish Copper
1.2-1.3"

male

female

Gorgon Copper
1.3-1.4"

Bronze Copper
1.3-1.4"

male

female

PURPLISH COPPER is common from spring to fall, mostly in moist meadows. The underside of the hindwing is marked with a faint red line. The larva feeds mostly on dock and knotweeds.

BRONZE COPPER frequents wet meadows. It is double-brooded and hibernates in the egg stage. The margin of the underside of the hindwing has a broad orange band. The larva feeds mostly on several species of dock and knotweed.

GORGON COPPER has only a midsummer brood. Its underside is typical of the coppers. The female resembles that of the Purplish Copper but is less bright. The larva feeds on *Eriogonum*.

Purplish

Bronze

Gorgon

1.3"

larva

pupa

The Harvester

HARVESTERS, though few in species, are world-wide in distribution. Only one occurs in N. America. The larva feeds on woolly aphids that live on alder, beech, and witch hazel, and becomes full-grown in as little as ten days. There are several generations a year. Winter is passed in the pupal stage on the ground. Markings of the pupa resemble a monkey's face.

BLUES are small and usually blue above. The larvae of some species secrete "honeydew" and are attended by ants for this liquid. There is much seasonal variation in color. The sexes differ; females usually are darker, with wider dark borders on the upperside of the wings.

male

underside

0.9-1.1"

larva

female

pupa

EASTERN TAILED BLUE, very common all through its range, occurs from early spring to fall, with several generations yearly. It overwinters as a full-grown larva, which feeds mostly on flowers of legumes. Males in spring have narrower dark borders above. Spring females are darker; some are brown above.

Eastern

Harvester

Pygmy Blue
0.5-0.7"

underside

male

Common Blue
0.8-1.3"

Dwarf Blue
0.5-0.7"

Common
Blue

Western
Tailed
Blue
0.9-1.1"

male—summer

male—spring

pupa

larva

Common Blue
female

PYGMY BLUES, and the Dwarf Blues, are the smallest of all North American butterflies. The Pygmy is common in its range. Its larva is well camouflaged on Lamb's Tongue, its food plant.

DWARF BLUE is similar but lacks the white spot and fringe on the upperside of the forewing.

COMMON BLUE, or Spring Azure, occurring throughout North America, is another early spring butterfly. Spring forms are darker than summer forms, with spots on the undersides sometimes fused. The underside markings of summer forms are usually pale. The slug-like larva feeds on flowers, especially those of dogwood. It is attended by ants for its "honeydew."

WESTERN TAILED BLUE is most easily told from Eastern by the fewer spots on the underside. Numerous similarities suggest that these two butterflies are forms of the same species.

71

(1)
male
0.7-1.1"

(2) underside

(3) female

(4)

(5)
0.7-1.0"

(8) underside

(6)
0.8-1.1"

(7) male
0.9-1.2"

(9) female

(1, 2, 3) MARINE BLUE appears later in spring than other blues. Larva feeds mostly on buds and blossoms of wisteria, alfalfa, locoweed, and other legumes.

(4, 5) ACMON BLUE occurs early spring to fall. The female is brownish or bluish. The broad orange band with black spots on hindwing is distinctive.

(6) REAKIRT'S BLUE is easily distinguished by the white-ringed black spots on the underside of the forewing. Mesquite is one of its food plants.

(7, 8, 9) ORANGE-BOR-DERED BLUE, or Melissa Blue, is double-brooded. Larva feeds on legumes. Note orange spots on upper hindwing of female.

(1) 0.9-1.2"

(2) female

(3) underside

(4) male 0.9-1.2"

(5) female

(6) underside

(7) male 0.9-1.0"

(8) female

(9) underside

(10) male 1.0-1.1"

(1) SILVERY BLUE lacks the black spots along the margin of underside of hindwing. The upperside resembles the light forms of the Saepiolus Blue.

(2, 3, 4) SAEPIOLUS BLUE is variable; some forms in the West are dark. The row of tiny orange spots on the underside of hindwing is distinctive.

(5, 6, 7) SONORA BLUE appears very early in spring. It is found near stonecrop *(Sedum)* and other succulent plants. Larva feeds in the thick plant tissues.

(8, 9, 10) SQUARE-SPOTTED BLUE occurs in June or July where its food, *Eriogonum*, grows. Black spots on underside are squarish. Resembles Acmon Blue.

Silvery

Sonora

Saepiolus

Square-spotted

73

SKIPPERS

Skippers (more than 2,000 kinds) are distinguished from true butterflies by the antennae, which are farther apart at the base and end in pointed, curved clubs. Skippers are named from their skipping flight. Most are drab. Their bodies are robust and moth-like. The larvae, with a neck-like constriction behind the head, rest during the day between leaves pulled together loosely by silk strands. The smooth pupae are formed in similar shelters, usually on the ground. Many are difficult to distinguish.

Silver-spotted Skipper
1.7-2.0"

1.5-1.8"

underside

larva

pupa

HOARY-EDGED, or Frosted Skipper, occurs from southern New England to Fla. and west to Tex. and Iowa. Underside resembles Silver-spotted. Larva feeds mostly on tick trefoils.

SILVER-SPOTTED SKIPPER, common throughout the warm seasons from so. Canada through Cen. Amer., has distinctive silver patch on the hindwing. The larva feeds on locusts and wisteria.

1.3-1.6"

1.6-2.0"

NORTHERN CLOUDY WING
is difficult to tell from Southern
Cloudy Wing. The spots on the
forewing are usually smaller and
the wing fringes are darker. It is
double-brooded in the North,
may have three or more broods
in the South, and overwinters in
the pupal stage. The green larva,
which lives in a silk-lined nest,
feeds on clover and other herbaceous legumes.

GOLDEN-BANDED SKIPPER
is generally uncommon and unusually sluggish. It occurs in wet
woodlands from N.Y. south and
west to Arizona. The larva is
light green with yellow dots.

LONG TAILED SKIPPER is
also called the Bean Leaf Roller
because of the way the larva attacks cultivated beans. Common
in the Southeast. It overwinters
as a pupa.

SOUTHERN CLOUDY WING
prefers woods margins, especially
near clover and other legumes
on which the brown larva feeds.
Note the larger white spots on
the forewings.

1.6-2.0"

1.3-1.6"

female

male
1.1-1.6"

0.9-1.3"

SLEEPY DUSKY-WING, unlike most other dusky-wings, has no clear spots on the forewing. Found from southern Canada to the Gulf and west to the Rockies.

DREAMY DUSKY-WING is smaller than Sleepy Dusky-wing; also has no clear spots on the forewing. Like the Sleepy, it occurs in early spring.

1.2-1.8"

JUVENAL'S DUSKY-WING occurs in woods margins in Sleepy's range in spring. Hindwing has two distinct white spots below. Female is paler than male.

1.0-1.3"

MARTIAL'S DUSKY-WING has white marks of upperside repeated below. Female is lighter than the male. Adults occur in late May and mid-July.

MOURNFUL DUSKY-WING of the West Coast has white dashes on the underside next to the white fringe on the hindwing.

FUNERAL DUSKY-WING, found southwest from Colo. and Tex., has white fringes on the hindwings. Larva feeds on alfalfa.

1.3-1.4"

Dreamy

Martial's

1.3-1.8"

1.0-1.3"

1.8-2.3"

CHECKERED SKIPPER, a common species, varies greatly in the amount of gray. Flies fast without the characteristic skipping motion. Larva feeds on mallows.

GRIZZLED SKIPPER resembles Checkered Skipper, but the forewing spots are somewhat square and separate; its underside is darker. Also feeds on mallows.

BRAZILIAN SKIPPER (or Larger Canna Leaf Roller) ranges from Argentina north to Tex., So. Car., and occasionally northward. Larva feeds on opening leaves of cannas; may be destructive.

Southern Sooty-wing 1.0-1.3"

pupa

0.8-1.1"

Common Sooty-wing with larva and pupa 1.0-1.2"

larva

COMMON SOOTY-WING occurs throughout North America. It overwinters as a larva on the food plant, pigweed, between leaves that have been rolled together with silk.

SOUTHERN SOOTY-WING is like the Common but has faint dark bands on the wings. Occurs from Pa. to Nebr. and the S.E. Larva feeds on Lamb's Quarter.

Grizzled

Checkered

77

0.7-1.0"

underside

1.0-1.4"

LEAST SKIPPER, common east of the Rockies from spring to fall, flies close to the ground, usually in marshy areas. It varies in the amount of orange above.

UNCAS SKIPPER of the Great Plains can be recognized by the dark patches around the white spots on the underside of the hindwing.

COBWEB SKIPPER occurs in early spring from Wisconsin and Texas eastward. It and the Indian Skipper resemble Uncas Skipper.

JUBA SKIPPER is found in sagebrush regions from the Pacific coastal states east to Colorado. Seen in both spring, fall.

1.0-1.3"

1.3-1.4"

1.0-1.4"

INDIAN SKIPPER appears in early spring in eastern United States and Canada. Larva feeds on Panic Grass.

LEONARD'S SKIPPER, a late summer, eastern species, frequents wet meadows and open regions. The larva feeds on grass and overwinters when small.

GOLDEN SKIPPER of the arid Southwest occurs from April to September. The underside is plain yellow. Larva feeds on Bermuda Grass (Cynodon dactylon).

1.1-1.4"

underside

0.7-1.0"

BROKEN DASH is named for the dash mark on upperside of male's forewing. Unlike Peck's, it is broken into a long upper mark and a lower dot. Both sexes lack Peck's yellow patches on undersides. Found east of Rockies.

LONG DASH has an irregular, dark, oblique mark on forewing of male. Yellow areas, less distinct than in Peck's, occur on undersides in both sexes. Long Dash occurs from Virginia and Illinois north into Canada.

VERNAL SKIPPER, or Little Glassy Wing, is a midsummer species found east of the Rockies. Female resembles male. The larva feeds on grass.

PECK'S SKIPPER occurs from so. Canada and New Eng. south to Fla. and west to Kans. and Ariz. Undersides of both sexes have distinct yellow patches.

FIERY SKIPPER has characteristic short antennae and varies in color pattern. The female is dark brown with a few light spots above.

FIELD SKIPPER, or Sachem, occurs in the South in spring. By midsummer it ranges to N.Y., N. Dak., and San Francisco. Larva feeds on Bermuda Grass.

male
1.1-1.3"

Zabulon Skipper
1.1-1.3"
male

"Pocahontas"
dark female

female
underside

female

HOBOMOK SKIPPER occurs from Kansas to southern Canada. Female has two color forms, one like the male and the other, or "Pocahontas," being quite dark and different above.

ROADSIDE SKIPPER has hindwings without markings. Wing fringes are strongly checkered. It occurs from southeast Canada to Florida and west to California. The pupa winters on grass.

ZABULON SKIPPER is found from Massachusetts to Texas. Male resembles Hobomok and female looks like the Pocahontas form of Hobomok. Zabulon and Hobomok both feed on grasses.

OCOLA SKIPPER ranges as far north as N.Y., and is common from Virginia and Arkansas south to Florida and Texas. The markings of its forewings are repeated on the underside.

0.8-1.1"

1.1-1.4"

1.8-3.3"

◀ **YUCCA SKIPPER** occurs in semi-arid regions from the Carolinas to Florida and west to California. Females are larger than males, with a row of four yellow spots on the hindwing. Both have broad wings and stout bodies. Larva feeds on yucca stalks.

80

MOTHS

The 8,000 or so species of moths which occur in North America north of Mexico have bodies more plump and furry than those of butterflies. At rest, moths usually hold their wings flat or fold them roof-like over their backs. Their antennae, often feathery, vary in structure but usually lack the terminal club typical of butterflies. Most moths have a frenulum, a curved

PLEBEIAN SPHINX occurs throughout eastern North America. The larva, active at night, feeds on the Trumpet Vine. See pp. 82-94 for other sphinxes.

2.5-3.0"

spine or group of bristles on the inner (humeral) angle of the hindwing. This helps to hold the fore and hindwings together in flight. Most moths fly at night and are attracted to lights. A few female moths do not fly at all. Larvae of moths spin silken cocoons or pupate on the ground or in underground cells.

In this section, moths are treated as commonly recognized groups which usually, but not always, include closely related species.

Below: Types of moth antennae. *Right:* Underwing Moth: underside of wings showing frenulum.

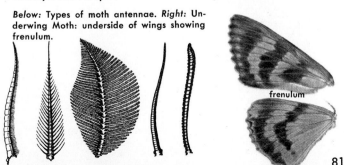

frenulum

81

SPHINX MOTHS, about 100 N. A. species have large, stout larvae that hold the front of their bodies erect like a sphinx. Most larvae have a horn at the rear of their body. Adults are powerful fliers; they often have a long proboscis with which they suck nectar. Some are called hawkmoths for their swooping flight; others hummingbird moths because they hover while feeding.

PINK-SPOTTED HAWK-MOTH ranges throughout most of the Western Hemisphere. The larva, or Sweetpotato Hornworm, feeds on Sweet Potato vines and closely related plants. This hawkmoth is a strong flier and has been seen far at sea.

3.2-4.5"

CAROLINA SPHINX can be readily told from the Five-spotted Hawkmoth by the partial fusion of the two middle black stripes on the hindwing. The larva, or Tobacco Hornworm, feeds on tobacco and tomatoes throughout the U.S. The pupa, formed underground, has a longer tongue case than the Tomato Hornworm's.

larva
Tobacco Hornworm
3.5-4.5"

wing stripes fused

RUSTIC SPHINX, or Six-spotted Sphinx, is common in southern states. On the sides of the body are three pairs of yellow spots. Larva resembles Tobacco and Tomato Hornworms, but the skin is rough instead of smooth where the markings appear. Feeds mainly on the Fringe Tree and jasmine.

4.0-5.0"

Tomato
Hornworm
larva

FIVE-SPOTTED HAWK-MOTH, unlike Carolina Sphinx, has black stripes on hindwing separated. Larva, the common Tomato Hornworm, feeds also on tobacco. The white mark on each abdominal segment forms an angle instead of a single oblique line as on the Tobacco Hornworm. Widespread in temperate N.A.

pupa

3.5-4.5"

wing stripes separated

83

◀ **WAVED SPHINX** resembles the Catalpa Sphinx but is brighter, with more white scales on the forewings. The larva, which feeds mostly on ash but also on privet and lilac, is green and smooth. It has the oblique marks typical of sphinx larvae and often has pink legs, horn, and face.

3.0-4.3"

wings folded

Catalpa Sphinx

2.3-3.8"
wings open

dark larva

CATALPA SPHINX as a larva is the destructive Catalpaworm, which when numerous strips catalpa trees of all foliage. The moths lay masses of white eggs on the undersides of the leaves. The velvety larvae occur in two color forms, as shown. There are commonly two broods each year. The larvae are so highly subject to attack by a parasitic wasp that few of them survive to become pupae and moths.

light larva

84

FOUR-HORNED SPHINX, or Elm Sphinx, occurs from Canada to Va. and west through the Miss. Valley. Adult has paler color on front margin of forewing than Catalpa and Waved Sphinx. The larva, which feeds on elm or birch, has four green or brown rough projections on the thoracic segments.

3.0-4.8"

4-horned Sphinx larva on elm

HERMIT SPHINX larva, which feeds on mints, has an unusual pyramidal hump toward its front end. The Hermit-like Sphinx, a moth of the Southwest, is very similar but is light gray and lacks the black stripe on its middle.

PAWPAW SPHINX is brown of varying shades, with small white spots on each side of the center abdominal stripe. The larva feeds on leaves of Pawpaw and Black Alder.

2.3-3.0"

Hermit

Pawpaw

1.8-2.8"

85

3.3-4.3"

ELEGANT SPHINX is much like the Great Ash Sphinx but is a darker gray. These moths are frequently seen at evening primrose flowers. The larva is sometimes a pest of apple and plum trees.

larva

3.8-4.5"

GREAT ASH SPHINX, or Pen-marked Sphinx, gets the latter name from the black wavy streaks on the forewings. Its thorax is lighter than that of the Apple Sphinx or Wild Cherry Sphinx and lacks the white streaks on the sides. The larva feeds mostly on ash trees but also on lilac and privet. It is double-brooded in some areas, but in others it occurs in all stages from spring to fall.

Elegant

Great Ash

LAUREL SPHINX, in spite of its name, feeds mostly on the leaves of lilac and Fringe Trees. It closely resembles the Apple and Wild Cherry Sphinx Moths in form but has a distinct brown color.

3.3-4.3"

2.5-3.5"

APPLE SPHINX resembles the Wild Cherry Sphinx but lacks both the white shading along the front edge of the forewing and the black band down the side of the abdomen. It occurs in midsummer. The larva is bright green and has seven slanted white lines edged with pink. It feeds mainly on apple, ash, wild rose, Myrtle and Sweet Fern.

3.0-4.5"

WILD CHERRY SPHINX looks much like Apple Sphinx but has a lateral black band on the abdomen. The larva feeds on cherry, plum, and apple. Unlike most other hawkmoth larvae, it hides during the day. It is darker than the larva of Great Ash Sphinx and has violet body stripes. In the Apple Sphinx these are pinkish; in the Laurel Sphinx they are often bluish marked with black.

ELLO SPHINX is common from the Gulf states into the tropics and often strays northward. Females lack the dark streaks in the forewings. The larva feeds mostly on cassava.

larva

2.8-4.0"

1.8-2.3"

ABBOT'S PINE SPHINX is similar to the Bombyx, which occupies about the same range. Abbot's larva, also like that of Bombyx, feeds on pines and it, too, may become destructive.

BOMBYX SPHINX larva feeds on White, Pitch, and Jack pines and sometimes is abundant enough to cause damage. Larva has a triangular head and lacks the typical caudal horn.

1.8-2.8"

Big Poplar Sphinx
3.5-5.5"

2.3-2.8"

Abbot's Sphinx
mature larva
1.8-2.3"

young larva

Abbot's Sphinx

BIG POPLAR SPHINX occurs in both a pale and a darker form. The larva has a rough, granular skin and an unusually short caudal horn. It feeds on poplars and willows.

ABBOT'S SPHINX has two forms of mature larva, one shown above and another bright green with brown spots. Young larvae are like that illustrated. Larvae feed on grape and woodbine.

SEQUOIA SPHINX was first found resting on a Sequoia tree and was so named. It frequents the blossoms of Wild Cherry and buckeye. The larva feeds on Wild Cherry leaves.

Sequoia

Abbot's

1.8-2.3"

CERISY'S SPHINX is darker and more common in the western part of its range. Larva (on willow) resembles the Small-eyed Sphinx but lacks red spots and has a pink, violet, or blue horn.

2.3-3.3"

2.0-2.8"

HUCKLEBERRY SPHINX may be confused with Small-eyed Sphinx, but the outer edge of the forewing is straight instead of concave. The larva feeds on blueberry and huckleberry.

◀ **SMALL-EYED SPHINX** and other eye-spotted sphinxes rest with a lobe of the hindwing extending before the forewing and with the abdomen of the male curved upward. Spots on the larva vary or may be absent. Prefers Wild Cherry but also feeds on birch and other trees. Occurs from southern Canada to Georgia and west to the Rockies.

2.0-2.5"

wings open

larva

wings folded

Cerisy's

Huckleberry

2.0-2.8"

2.3-2.8"

TWIN-SPOTTED SPHINX gets its name from the blue bar across each eyespot on the hindwing. Larva cannot be told from that of Cerisy's Sphinx. It feeds on Wild Cherry, birch, and willow.

BLIND-EYED SPHINX larva feeds on a wide variety of trees but prefers birch, willow, and cherry. It varies in color and cannot be told from the larva of the Small-eyed Sphinx.

WALNUT SPHINX is a relatively common sphinx moth found from New England south to Florida and west to Manitoba and Texas. The active larva feeds only on walnut, Butternut, pecan, and hickory, and is sometimes common in pecan orchards. The moths vary considerably in color. The larvae vary in color also, from green to reddish.

1.8-2.8"

larva

Twin-spotted

Blind-eyed

1.8-2.0"

2.0-2.8"

NESSUS SPHINX flies at early dusk. The larva resembles that of the Hog Sphinx but has a shorter horn and more oblique marks on the side of the body. It feeds on grape and Virginia Creeper.

AZALEA SPHINX resembles the Hog Sphinx also, but the forewing is brown instead of greenish and the hindwings are entirely orange-brown. The larva feeds on viburnum and azalea.

HOG SPHINX, or Virginia-Creeper Sphinx, shown at rest, has hindwings almost entirely bright orange-brown. It is common and sometimes becomes a pest in vineyards. Unlike most hawkmoth larvae that burrow in the ground to pupate, a Hog Sphinx larva forms a loose cocoon of silk among dead leaves on the ground.

HYDRANGEA SPHINX occurs in much the same range as Hog Sphinx. At rest it assumes the position shown for Hog Sphinx. The larva feeds on hydrangea, Buttonbush, and Swamp Loosestrife.

2.0-2.8"

larva

Hog Sphinx

2.0-2.8"

pupa

Nessus

Azalea and Hog

3.0-4.0"

Pandora Sphinx larva

ACHEMON SPHINX larva resembles that of Pandora Sphinx except that the spots on the sides of the body are long and angular instead of oval. This species feeds on grape and Virginia Creeper.

Lesser Vine Sphinx

3.3-4.3"

3.0-4.5"

▲

PANDORA SPHINX, when an almost half-grown larva, loses its horn and acquires a glassy eyespot in its place. The larva, green or reddish brown, feeds on grape and Virginia Creeper.

LESSER VINE SPHINX, a tropical species, strays into New Eng. Larva feeds on grape and Va. Creeper. It is marked with black, white, and red, and has an eyespot in place of a horn.

Achemon   Pandora

93

1.5-2.5"

larva

Hummingbird Moth

Bumblebee Moth 1.3-1.8"

White-lined Sphinx 2.0-3.5"

larva

Galium Sphinx

2.0-2.8"

HUMMINGBIRD MOTH, or Common Clearwing, varies in color with season and race. The "clear" wing results as scales wear off soon after the moth emerges. Feeds at flowers by day.

BUMBLEBEE MOTH also has seasonal and racial forms. It differs from the Hummingbird Moth in having an unscaled cell on the front edge of the forewing near the body.

WHITE-LINED SPHINX, or Striped Morning Sphinx, often flies by day. The larva is sometimes green with a series of yellow spots. When abundant it is a pest, feeding on many broad-leaved plants from southern Canada into Central America.

GALIUM SPHINX is from the Old World. The larva has two color forms like the White-lined Sphinx's. In Europe it feeds on bedstraw *(Galium)* but in America mainly on *Epilobium* and other plants.

3.0-5.3"

CYNTHIA MOTH, introduced from China, is found mostly near cities from Boston to Washington, D.C. The larva, which feeds on Ailanthus, resembles the Cecropia except that all tubercles are bluish. The cocoons hang like those of the Promethea Moth.

GIANT SILK MOTHS, most of which are large and attractive, number about 42 species north of Mexico. Some have clear spots, or "windows," in their wings. In some the sexes differ in size and color, but males can always be told by their more feathery antennae. The proboscis is barely developed, indicating that adults do not feed. The hindwing has no frenulum. The larva, which feeds mostly on leaves of trees and shrubs, is ornately armed with tubercles and spines. The cocoon, long and oval, is made of silk and is attached to the food plants. Easily spotted in winter. These night-flying moths come to lights, and unmated females attract distant males. You can obtain specimens and study mating, egg laying, and growth by placing a newly emerged female in an out-of-doors cage and waiting for the males to reach the cage.

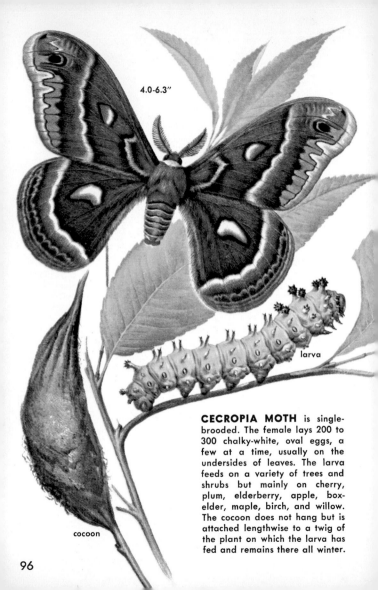

4.0-6.3"

larva

cocoon

CECROPIA MOTH is single-brooded. The female lays 200 to 300 chalky-white, oval eggs, a few at a time, usually on the undersides of leaves. The larva feeds on a variety of trees and shrubs but mainly on cherry, plum, elderberry, apple, box-elder, maple, birch, and willow. The cocoon does not hang but is attached lengthwise to a twig of the plant on which the larva has fed and remains there all winter.

Glover's Silk Moth
3.5-5.0"

Ceanothus Silk Moth
3.5-5.0"

GLOVER'S SILK MOTH is in all early stages resembles the Cecropia, but the larva has yellow instead of red thoracic tubercles. It feeds on cherry, maple, boxelder, and other plants.

CEANOTHUS SILK MOTH is single-brooded. The larva resembles that of Cecropia, but it has yellow thoracic tubercles with black rings. It prefers buckbush (Ceanothus) leaves.

3.3-4.0"

Columbian
Silk Moth

larva

Pandora Moth
2.0-3.3"

COLUMBIAN SILK MOTH
larva has red thoracic tubercles
like that of Cecropia, but they
are ringed with black at the
base. The cocoon, attached
lengthwise, has silvery streaks.
Adult resembles a small Cecropia
Moth but lacks reddish margins
to the white wing bands.

PANDORA MOTH, a pest of
pine forests, has a two-year life
cycle. The first winter is spent as
a partly grown larva on trees
and the second as a pupa in the
ground. No cocoon is spun.

Columbian

Pandora

Eggs laid June 3, 1957
Hatched July 13
Started cocoon July 13

3.5-5.5"

larva

cocoon

POLYPHEMUS MOTH, perhaps the commonest giant silk moth, was named after the one-eyed giant Polyphemus of Greek mythology because of the large eyespots on its hindwings. In the South it has two broods. The accordion-shaped larva feeds on a variety of trees and shrubs, especially on oak, hickory, elm, maple, and birch. The rounded, tough, parchment-like cocoon is found hanging on the food plant.

female

cocoon

male
2.5-4.0"

larva

PROMETHEA MOTH, also called the Spicebush Silk Moth, was once considered as a possible source of silk in an American silk industry. Males fly in the late afternoon—an unusual habit. Spicebush, Sassafras, Tuliptree, and Wild Cherry are preferred foods of the larva. The cocoon is always suspended on the food plant, where it is easily seen and can be found in winter. There are two broods each year.

Promethea

female

male
2.8-4.0"

cocoon

TULIP-TREE SILK MOTH
larva feeds mostly on Tuliptrees.
It resembles the Promethea larva
but has fewer and shorter tubercles. The cocoon is not fas-
tened to the food plant as with
most other large silk moths. The
male looks more like its mate
than does the male Promethea.
The Tulip-tree Silk Moth flies only
at night. This moth is also double-
brooded but is not very common
anywhere in its range.

Tulip-tree

3.2-4.5"

cocoon

larva

LUNA MOTH has seasonal forms where it is double-brooded. The summer form has yellow wing margins, instead of pink to purple, which show on those emerging in spring. Larva feeds mainly on Sweet Gum, hickory, walnut, and persimmon. Pupa is active in its papery cocoon, usually spun on the ground.

male
2.0-3.0"

female

Io Moth
and larva

IO MOTH, named for a mythical Greek maiden, has conspicuous eyespots on the hindwings. Eggs are laid in clusters. The larvae stay together and move in long trains. They feed on a wide variety of plants, including corn and roses. The larvae, with very irritating spines, spin thin, papery cocoons on the ground.

DAY MOTH eggs, laid in masses around twigs, hatch in the spring. The larva feeds mainly on plants of the rose family. When mature it is brownish-black with tan and black spines, red spots down the middle, and a red line on each side. Pupates early. The moth emerges in the summer, some in the second summer.

Day Moth
1.8-3.0"

Day

Io

1.5-2.8"

BUCK MOTH flies by day. In fall, females lay eggs in clusters around a twig, usually oak. The eggs hatch in spring. Like those of the Io, Buck larvae feed together and have stinging spines. Larvae do not spin cocoons but burrow into the ground and pupate. Most moths emerge in fall, some the next spring or the following fall.

larva

eggs

1.8-3.0"

NEVADA BUCK MOTH is like the Buck Moth in most respects. The larva is greenish instead of gray and has brown spots on each side of the back and along the sides of the body. The spiracles are yellow, edged with brown. The larva feeds on willow and poplar. Moths are found from September to November.

Nevada Buck

Range Caterpillar

RANGE CATERPILLAR, a serious range pest in the Southwest, feeds on grasses and sometimes attacks corn and other crops. Moths occur in the fall and, although day-flying, are attracted to lights at night. The eggs are laid in masses around plant stems. The cocoon is of loosely joined plant fragments.

1.5-2.5"

TRUE SILK MOTHS are not native to North America. The silkworm that produces the silk used for thread comes from Asia, where the Chinese first learned to unravel the silk from cocoons some 5,000 years ago. In commercial silk production the moths are induced to lay eggs on cards. The eggs hatch in about 10 days, and the "worms" are fed mulberry leaves. They eat steadily until in about a month the silkworm becomes full-grown. Soon every larva is ready to spin a cocoon. A few cocoons are allowed to develop into moths, but most are placed in boiling water so they can be unraveled easily. The single strand of silk that makes each cocoon may be from 500 to 1,300 yards long. They are combined to make a thread not yet duplicated by any synthetic fibers.

larva

cocoon

1.3-1.8"

Silk Moth

REGAL, OR ROYAL, MOTHS are medium- to large-sized. There are fewer than twenty species in America north of Mexico. Caterpillars, generally spiny, feed on many kinds of trees. Larvae of some species are destructive to forests and shade plantings. The caterpillars do not spin cocoons but burrow into the ground, where the pupa is formed. At rest, Regal Moths usually fold their wings roof-like over their bodies. Like silk moths they are not attracted to bait but are attracted to lights.

larva

1.8-2.5"

larva

HONEY-LOCUST MOTH varies in the color of its wings and in the presence or absence of forewing markings. The larva feeds on Honey Locust and Kentucky Coffee Tree. This moth is double-brooded. It overwinters as a pupa in the ground.

◀ **ROSY MAPLE MOTH** larva, called the Green-striped Maple Worm, overwinters as a pupa. Like oakworms (p. 107) they feed in large colonies and sometimes strip Red and Silver maples of their leaves. There are two broods yearly.

1.0-2.0"

Rosy

Honey

OAKWORM MOTHS are easier to tell apart as larvae than as adults. Larvae feed in colonies, sometimes so many as to completely strip forests. Females are larger than males, with thinner antennae and stouter bodies.

ORANGE-STRIPED OAK-WORM The male has angular shaped hindwings. The forewings of the female are thinner and less speckled than those of the female Spiny Oakworm.

larva

Orange-striped Oakworm
1.0-2.0"

female

Spiny Oakworm
1.5-2.5"

larva

SPINY OAKWORM The male moth closely resembles the female. It is the largest of the species illustrated, and sexes are more alike than the others.

PINK-STRIPED OAKWORM Male has narrower, more triangular forewings, thinner beyond the spot than other species. Female lacks spotting on wings.

Spiny, Orange-striped and Pink-striped

1.5-2.3"

3.5-5.5"

ROYAL WALNUT MOTH The larva is called the Hickory Horned Devil for its frightful appearance and for its food plant— hickory. It also feeds on sumac and Sweet Gum. This moth, seen in midsummer, probably has only one brood a year. Note the wing veins, bordered by red scales.

larva

Imperial

Royal

female
3.3-5.5"

IMPERIAL MOTH is dimorphic, the female being much larger and yellower than the male. At rest their wings are partly spread, as shown. The larva, usually green but sometimes tan or dark brown, feeds mainly on oak, maple, pine, sycamore, Sweet Gum, and Sassafras. It is single-brooded.

larva

male

109

TIGER MOTHS are small to medium in size and generally light in color. Many have conspicuous spots or stripes. Only a few of some 200 species north of Mexico have functional mouthparts. Adults, especially males, come readily to lights. Most larvae are covered with a dense coat of hairs, which are shed and mixed with silk when the cocoon is made. Most caterpillars move about rapidly and are active by day. They commonly roll into a ball when disturbed.

GREAT LEOPARD MOTH is well named for its wing spots. The hairs on the caterpillar are very stiff, and crimson rings between segments show distinctly when the larva rolls into a ball. Feeds on plantain. Cocoon is spun in spring. Larva overwinters.

2.0-3.0"

rolled-up larva

1.8-2.5"

▲

ACREA MOTH larva, called the Salt Marsh Caterpillar, feeds on herbaceous plants. It is double-brooded. The larvae are often abundant in fall and over-winter as pupae in cocoons. Adult wings are profusely spotted. The female has white hindwings.

ISABELLA MOTH is not as well known as its caterpillar, the Woolly Bear. The amount of black on each end of its body does not foretell the severity of the coming winter. There are two broods; cocoons are formed in spring and summer.

1.5-2.0"

▼

larva

cocoon

Isabella

Acrea

Fall Webworm
0.8-1.5"

spotless

1.8-2.8"

larva

lightly spotted

heavily spotted

GARDEN TIGER MOTH is so variable that its forms look like different species. The hindwings may be yellow with dark spots, and the forewings may bear very broad white bands.

FALL WEBWORM is also variable. Some moths have heavily spotted wings. Others have only a few black dots. The bodies of some are yellow with black dots on the sides, while others are plain white. The social larvae extend their webs over the foliage of the many deciduous trees on which they feed. The webs may soon cover large branches. These webs are sometimes confused with those of tent caterpillars (p. 138). Large numbers of eggs are laid in masses, usually on the undersides of leaves. Pupae overwinter in cocoons.

Garden

Fall

1.5-2.0"

Arge Tiger Moth
larva

CLYMENE is a Haploa Tiger Moth, of which there are five species north of Mexico. In some the hindwings are white or buff. Clymene has one brood. The moths occur in midsummer.

APANTESIS TIGER MOTHS include some 30 species, often varying greatly in color. In general their forewings are jet black with irregular white streaks, and their hindwings are yellow or red with black spots or bands. The hairy caterpillars live over the winter and feed mostly on herbaceous plants. Males are commonly captured at lights.

ARGE is double-brooded, with moths occurring June and Sept.

VIRGO has a typical Apantesis color pattern. It is single-brooded, with moths on the wing mainly in July.

Arge Tiger Moth
1.3-2.0"

Virgo Tiger Moth
1.8-3.0"

113

HICKORY TIGER MOTH is a forest pest of hickory, walnut, and other trees. The moth is found in midsummer. Eggs are laid in masses, and the larvae feed in colonies but do not make webs. They may be common in late summer and fall.

1.3-2.3"

larva

◄SPOTTED TIGER MOTH has a life history similar to the Hickory Tiger Moth, but the larvae feed singly and prefer poplar and maple. The yellowish larvae may be black at ends.

1.5-2.0"

larva

◄PALE TIGER MOTH is also called the Banded Tiger Moth. The larva, from yellowish to gray, feeds on a variety of trees. Life history is like the Spotted Tiger's. It overwinters in a soft, hairy cocoon. The Sycamore Tiger Moth is very similar.

1.3-2.0"

Spotted

Hickory

Pale Tiger

YELLOW WOOLLY BEAR
larvae are seen more commonly than the adults. They vary from pale yellow to reddish and are confused with the Salt Marsh Caterpillar, but have black heads. There are two broods.

larva

1.0-1.8"

RANCHMAN'S TIGER MOTH ▶
is one of the largest and most attractive members of this group. Another common form of this moth has yellow hindwings and a yellow body.

2.0-3.0"

larva

DOGBANE TIGER MOTH ▶
varies in the amount of yellow on the front edge of the fore-wing. It is probably double-brooded. The caterpillar, with an unusually light hairlike covering, feeds almost entirely on dog-bane. May be very common.

1.3-1.8"

Yellow Woolly Bear

Ranchman's

Dogbane

Showy Holomelina
1.0-1.3"

Milkweed
Tiger
larva

1.0-1.8"

1.3-1.8"

larva

pupa

SHOWY HOLOMELINA is the brightest of the eight or so holomelina moths of North America. Others are mainly yellowish, gray, or dull red. The larva, like that of the Dogbane Moth, has a soft, hairlike covering. The cocoon is very thin, with few hairs.

◄ **MILKWEED TIGER MOTH** is better known by its larva, which is found in late summer feeding in colonies on milkweed. When disturbed it frequently rolls into a ball and drops from the plant. The pupa overwinters in a cocoon which is very hairy.

BELLA MOTH, or Rattlebox Moth, is locally common but is restricted to the vicinity of its food plant, Rattlebox, and other kinds of *Crotalaria*. The larva lacks the hairs typical of tiger moths. The pupa, which is unusually ornate, overwinters.

Milkweed

Showy   Bella

116

1.5-2.0"

Brown Ctenucha

larva

1.5-2.0"

Virginia Ctenucha

CTENUCHA MOTHS, daytime fliers, look like wasps when feeding at flowers. Larvae feed on marsh grasses. Hairy cocoons and larvae resemble those of some closely related tiger moths. Amounts of yellow and black hairs vary in Virginia Ctenucha larvae. Smaller, narrower-winged Brown Ctenucha Moth has a more southern range.

FORESTER MOTHS More than two dozen American species are known. They differ from most noctuid moths (p. 118) in having the ends of the antennae thickened. The Eight-spotted Forester is below. Its double-brooded larva feeds on grape and woodbine.

Eight-spotted Forester

1.0-1.5"

larva

DIOPTID MOTHS are represented by only one species in North America north of Mexico, the California Oakworm Moth. It is a pest of live oaks in California, sometimes stripping these trees.

The California Oakworm, brown with nearly transparent wings, is double-brooded. It overwinters as eggs or tiny larvae. The female California Oakworm Moth lacks the yellowish patch near the mid-forewing.

1.0-1.4"

California Oakworm larva

NOCTUID MOTHS (pp. 118-131) number over 2,600 kinds in America north of Mexico. Many are serious pests of farm and garden crops and forest and shade trees. Among these are the well-known armyworms, cutworms, and Corn Earworm. Noctuids vary greatly in habits, but most adults fly at night and feed on the nectar of flowers. Most noctuids are attracted to lights and to baits containing sugar. Some overwinter as pupae in the ground or in thin cocoons above ground. Others overwinter as larvae and a few as eggs or adults. They are sometimes called owlet moths, from the way their eyes shine in the dark when a light strikes them.

BLACK WITCH, or Giant Noctuid, is the largest of the family within our range. It is a tropical species, sometimes straying northward into Canada in the fall. Its shade of brown varies. The wings of the females come to a less sharp point at the apex. Larva feeds on acacia and similar plants. Considered a pest in Hawaii.

3.5-6.0"

AMERICAN DAGGER MOTH is the largest of the daggers. The larva feeds on a variety of trees. Winter is passed as a pupa, often in an old stump. The cocoon includes the hair of the larva.

2.0-2.8"

larva

DAGGER MOTHS (some 70 kinds) are so named for the dagger-like mark near the forewing outer margin. Adults are similar but many of the larvae are quite different. Some are hairy, with characteristic tufts of longer hair called pencils. Other larvae lack hair and may be spiny. Dagger moths overwinter as pupae.

1.3-1.8"

larva

1.3-1.8"

SMEARED DAGGER MOTH occurs more commonly in wetlands, where the larva feeds on willow, smartweed, alder, Buttonbush, and cattail. Overwintering cocoon is thin but strong.

COTTONWOOD DAGGER MOTH varies greatly in markings. Larva has soft yellow hair like American Dagger but has five hair pencils on its abdomen. It feeds on poplars and willows.

CUTWORM MOTHS are noctuids whose larvae, or cutworms, cut off young plants just above the ground. Some cutworms drag cut-off portions of plants into a hole. Some are climbers, feeding on foliage of bushes and trees. All feed at night. Certain species occur only in spring, others only in fall; many have several broods each year. Some full-grown larvae remain at rest without feeding from spring to late summer, when they pupate.

1.5-1.8"

1.5-2.3"

larva

BLACK CUTWORM, also called the Greasy Cutworm, occurs throughout the U.S. and southern Canada. Larva is a burrower, found mostly in low spots. Overwinters as a pupa.

SPOTTED CUTWORM is one of the most damaging, feeding on a wide variety of plants and often climbing them. It overwinters as a nearly mature larva. May have three broods yearly.

W-MARKED CUTWORM is a climber, feeding on a wide variety of trees, shrubs, and herbaceous plants. It overwinters as a larva and, in most areas, has two broods each year.

PALE-SIDED CUTWORM lives mostly in a tunnel into which it drags pieces of cut-off plants for food. There may be four broods yearly. The winter is passed in the pupal stage.

1.5-1.8"   1.5-1.8"

larva

1.3-1.5"

1.5-1.8"

PALE WESTERN CUTWORM moths occur in Aug. and Sept. and lay eggs on newly cultivated land. Overwintering may be as eggs or young larvae. Plants are attacked below the soil surface.

GLASSY CUTWORM occurs from Canada to N.J. and west to the Pacific. It feeds on roots and lower stems of grasses. It is single-brooded and overwinters as partly grown larva.

1.3-1.5"   larva   larva   1.3-1.5"

STRIPED GARDEN CUT-WORM is single-brooded. The moth occurs throughout most of U.S. in summer. Larvae rest exposed on food plants. They mature and pupate in fall.

SPOTTED-SIDED CUTWORM has one generation. The moth occurs from Alberta and Texas eastward in the fall. Full-grown larvae appear on dock and chickweed in early spring.

121

larva

1.3-1.5" 1.0-1.5"

DARK-SIDED CUTWORM is a climber, sometimes very destructive to orchards and shrubs. Eggs hatch during winter and larvae become full-grown by June. There is one brood.

STRIPED CUTWORM closely resembles Dark-sided Cutworm but differs much in life history. Eggs hatch in the fall and partly grown larvae hibernate in the soil, feeding again in spring.

1.3-2.0"

larva

1.3-1.5"

BRONZED CUTWORM prefers grasses and cereals. Moths occur in Sept. and Oct. and eggs hatch during winter. By April or May the larvae are full-grown, but they do not pupate until July.

WHITE CUTWORM sometimes damages the buds and young leaves of grapes and fruit trees. Its life history is like that of the Striped Cutworm. Head and spiracles of larva vary in color.

1.1-1.5"

0.8-1.0"

DINGY CUTWORM winters as immature larva, maturing in late spring. It lies inactive (estivates) until August, when it pupates, emerging as a moth in a month or so.

BRISTLY CUTWORM often occurs in clover with the Dingy Cutworm. It is double-brooded. Larva completes growth in the spring like that of Dingy Cutworm but does not estivate.

1.5-2.0"

1.0-1.8"

VARIEGATED CUTWORM, probably the most destructive cutworm, attacks many different crops. It overwinters as a pupa and may have four broods. Occurs throughout North America.

YELLOW-STRIPED ARMYWORM, also called Cotton Cutworm because it bores into cotton bolls, is common in the South. Feeds on many plants. Winter is passed as a pupa.

1.0-1.5"

larva

1.3-1.8"

larva

FALL ARMYWORM by mid-summer spreads north from the Gulf states but dies out by winter. In the South there may be three broods. Prefers grasses and often attacks corn.

ARMYWORM has two or more broods. The spring one is most destructive, especially to oats and small grains. Natural enemies reduce later broods. It overwinters as moth, pupa, or larva.

ARMYWORM MOTHS are noctuid moths whose larvae tend to migrate in "armies" to new feeding areas after destroying vegetation in fields where their eggs were laid. Active at night and hiding by day, the larvae feed mostly on grasses and small grains.

BEET ARMYWORM is a common pest of sugar beets in the West. Larva resembles that of Fall Armyworm, but the pale central line along the back is less distinct. Overwinters as pupa.

WHEAT HEAD ARMYWORM feeds mainly on timothy and wheat heads, attacking at night. Full-grown larva is about one inch long with narrow pale stripes. Overwinters as a pupa.

0.8-1.3"

1.0-1.5"

1.3-1.8"

1.3-1.8"

larva

ARMY CUTWORM sometimes occurs in vast numbers and travels in huge armies. Moths emerge in late summer and lay eggs in the soil. Young larva overwinters. Two forms of adult shown above.

ZEBRA CATERPILLAR feeds on a wide variety of garden and field crops. There are usually two broods each year, moths occurring in May and August. Overwinters in pupal stage.

1.0-1.5"

0.8-1.5"

COTTON LEAFWORM is a slender, looping larva that feeds only on cotton. Spines at end of the moth's tongue sometimes injure ripe fruit. This tropical species cannot survive U.S. winters.

GREEN CLOVERWORM, a looping larva, feeds on clover, alfalfa, and other legumes. Winter is usually passed as an adult but some may winter as a pupa. There are two to four broods.

125

ALFALFA LOOPER, in spite of its name, feeds on a wide variety of plants, including cereals. Winter is passed in pupal and adult stages. There are two broods, the second in July.

CABBAGE LOOPER, a common species, feeds mostly on cabbage and other members of the cabbage family. Two broods occur in the North. Hibernates as pupa in loosely woven cocoon.

LOOPERS is a name most commonly used for larvae of geometer moths (p. 140), but larvae of some noctuid moths are also called loopers because they hump their backs when crawling. The noctuid larvae have fewer than the normal four pairs of prolegs and claspers.

CELERY LOOPER in the larval stage closely resembles the Cabbage Looper. There are at least two broods. The summer form is brown, as illustrated. A spring form is gray.

BILOBED LOOPER feeds on alfalfa, clover, and many other plants. Larva resembles Cabbage Looper's but has stripes on the sides of its head. It hibernates as a pupa in a thin cocoon.

1.3-1.8"

1.0-1.5"

1.5-2.0"

1.3-1.8"

FORAGE LOOPER is sometimes destructive to clover. Markings of forewings are much less distinct in females. Three broods occur from spring to fall. Pupa overwinters on leaves.

GREEN FRUITWORM eats into young apples, pears, cherries, and other fruit in spring. Moths emerge in the fall and overwinter. The larva resembles that of Copper Underwing (p. 130).

LUNATE MOTH often has large green patches on the wing margins. Pupa overwinters in soil. The larva varies greatly in color and looks like those of the underwing moths (p. 128).

DRIED LEAF MOTH, or Litter Moth, larva feeds on lichens and dead leaves. The development from tiny eggs is very slow. The moths are on the wing in midsummer and are single-brooded.

0.8-1.5"

1.3-1.5"

larva

WIDOW UNDERWING is one of some seventeen catocala moths with plain dark brown underwings. This caterpillar feeds mostly on walnut and hickory.

2.8-3.0"

UNDERWING, OR CATOCALA, MOTHS (about 100 kinds in America north of Mexico) readily come to light and bait. Otherwise they would rarely be seen, for in daylight they rest well camouflaged on tree trunks with their underwings hidden. Larvae also rest by day on trunks or limbs, or under debris on the ground where the thin cocoons are also found. They have one brood and overwinter as eggs on bark of trees.

2.5-3.0"

WHITE UNDERWING varies greatly in the forewing pattern. The caterpillar closely resembles that of the Widow Underwing but feeds on willow and poplar.

128

2.5-3.3"

AHOLIBAH UNDERWING is hard to tell from several other catocala moths. Note its large size, with a wingspread occasionally exceeding three inches. Larva feeds on oak. It lacks the striped saddle patch of the Widow Underwing larva.

TINY NYMPH UNDERWING is one of several species of small catocalas with similar yellow underwings. The forewings vary greatly in pattern. The larva feeds on oak.

PENITENT UNDERWING flies from July to October. Larva lacks the fringe of hairs and swollen saddle patch of the Widow Underwing caterpillar larva. Feeds on walnut and hickory.

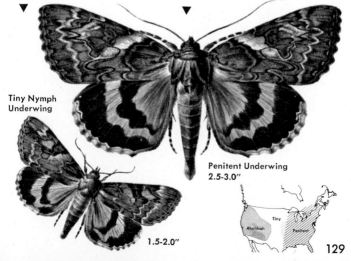

Tiny Nymph Underwing

Penitent Underwing
2.5-3.0"

1.5-2.0"

2.0-2.8"

larva

LOCUST UNDERWING is not a catocala moth, despite its name, but closely resembles one. The larva feeds on Black Locust. This species is double-brooded. It overwinters in the pupal stage.

larva

1.0-1.5"

1.5-2.0"

larva

COPPER UNDERWING occurs from midsummer to fall but hides in cracks during the day. In the spring, larva feeds on many plants, including Woodbine. It, too, is not a catocala underwing.

PEARLY WOOD NYMPH is one of three wood nymphs. Beautiful Wood Nymph is larger and has a dark margin on the hindwing. Calif. Wood Nymph has a black dot on hindwing.

White-veined Dagger larva

White-veined Dagger   1.0-1.8"

WHITE-VEINED DAGGER resembles the Smeared Dagger (p. 119) in the larval stage but has finer hair. Feeds on marsh plants, especially cattail. Cocoon is made in folded leaves.

Corn Earworm larva

larva

1.0-1.8"

1.3-1.5"

STALK BORER, a pest of corn, feeds in the stalks of many plants, especially Giant Ragweed. Eggs laid in fall hatch very early in spring. Bright body stripes are lost as the larva matures in summer. There is only one generation annually.

CORN EARWORM, the familiar worm in ears of corn, is also called Tomato Fruitworm and Bollworm. Larvae are often found in the fruit of many plants. Winter is passed as a pupa in the soil. There may be several broods each year.

THE PROMINENTS, numbering about 100 species north of Mexico, resemble noctuids. Readily attracted to lights. Many of them can be told by their hairy legs when at rest. Larvae of most species live on tree leaves. Many species lack anal prolegs and hold their rear ends erect.

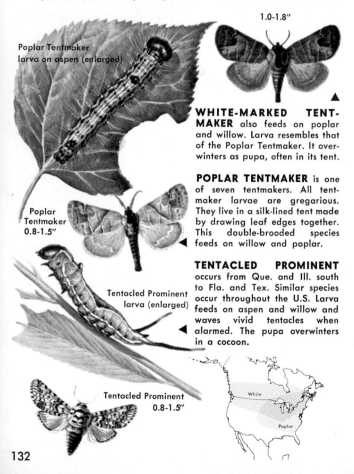

1.0-1.8"

Poplar Tentmaker
larva on aspen (enlarged)

Poplar
Tentmaker
0.8-1.5"

Tentacled Prominent
larva (enlarged)

Tentacled Prominent
0.8-1.5"

WHITE-MARKED TENT-MAKER also feeds on poplar and willow. Larva resembles that of the Poplar Tentmaker. It overwinters as pupa, often in its tent.

POPLAR TENTMAKER is one of seven tentmakers. All tentmaker larvae are gregarious. They live in a silk-lined tent made by drawing leaf edges together. This double-brooded species feeds on willow and poplar.

TENTACLED PROMINENT occurs from Que. and Ill. south to Fla. and Tex. Similar species occur throughout the U.S. Larva feeds on aspen and willow and waves vivid tentacles when alarmed. The pupa overwinters in a cocoon.

White

Poplar

characteristic pose of larva

larva

YELLOW-NECKED CATER-PILLAR feeds on many kinds of trees, preferring apple. Unlike most hand-maid moths, it has a scalloped outer margin on the forewing.

1.5-2.3"

HAND-MAID MOTHS number 12 species that re-semble one another closely. The larvae feed in colonies and may be numerous enough to strip trees. When dis-turbed they hold both ends of their bodies erect. Most species are single-brooded, overwintering as pupae in the ground. The Walnut Caterpillar feeds on walnut and hickory. The Sumac Caterpillar feeds only on sumac. The outer margins of the forewings of these two moths are straight. The moth of the Walnut Caterpillar is dark.

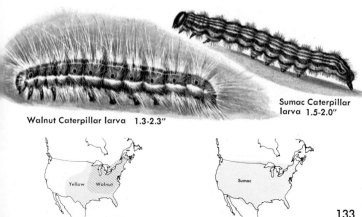

Sumac Caterpillar larva 1.5-2.0"

Walnut Caterpillar larva 1.3-2.3"

Yellow   Walnut

Sumac

larva

Variable
Oak Leaf 1.3-1.8"

larva

SADDLED PROMINENT is so named for the saddle mark on the back of the green, pointed-tailed larva, which feeds mainly on leaves of beech and maple. The moth resembles that of the Variable Oak Leaf Caterpillar.

VARIABLE OAK LEAF CATERPILLAR, found in late summer and fall, may lay 500 eggs singly, on oak. Larva overwinters in the soil and pupates in spring.

larva

1.3-1.5"

ANGUINA MOTH is commonly recognized by its unusual caterpillar, which feeds on various legumes, especially locust. The Anguina Moth is double-brooded.

larva

ELM LEAF CATERPILLAR is well camouflaged on elm foliage. Moths occur in June and August. Pupae spend winter in cocoons on the ground.

1.3-1.5"

Saddled

Variable

Elm

Anguina

RED-HUMPED CATERPILLAR is double-brooded. The moth lays eggs in masses on the undersides of apple, cherry, and other leaves. The larvae are gregarious. Cocoons overwinter on the ground; pupate in spring.

larva

1.0-1.5"

UNICORN CATERPILLAR has a life history similar to the Red-humped Caterpillar's, but it is not gregarious and feeds mostly on Wild Cherry and willow.

larva

1.0-1.5"

.5-2.3"

larva

ROUGH PROMINENT is double-brooded only in the northern part of its range. The larva, which feeds mostly on oaks, pupates in the soil.

RED-HUMPED OAKWORM is gregarious only as young larva. It feeds on varieties of oaks and is double-brooded in the South. The cocoon is spun on the ground.

larva

1.0-1.8"

Unicorn and Red-humped Caterpillar

Prominent

Red-humped Oakworm

135

1.3-2.3"

pupa

SATIN MOTH is Eurasian. Found in Mass. and Br. Columbia in 1920, it has spread through N.E. and N.W. U.S. and Canada. In July eggs are laid in masses. Larva prefers poplar and willow. It hibernates when partly grown.

larva

TUSSOCK MOTHS, numbering about 30 species, get their name from the brightly colored tufts of hair on the larvae. Hairs of some species are irritating. Adult legs are hairy. Some females are almost wingless. The antennae of males are feathery. Tussock moths have no tongue. Several tussock moths, including the Satin and Gypsy Moths, are pests of forest and shade trees.

female

GYPSY MOTH, accidentally introduced from Europe about 1868, spread through most of New England, with outbreaks in nearby states. It overwinters as eggs. Larva feeds on many deciduous trees, becomes full-grown in July.

pupa

shed skin

larva

male
1.0-2.5"

egg mass

male
0.8-1.5"

wingless female

larva

WHITE-MARKED TUSSOCK MOTH is a serious pest of many deciduous trees. It is double-brooded. The wingless female lays eggs, which overwinter, on her cocoon. The pupal stage lasts about 2 weeks.

WESTERN TUSSOCK MOTH is single-brooded, overwinters as eggs on the cocoon. Larva feeds on many trees and sometimes damages apples. Except for black heads and crimson prolegs, it resembles larva of White-marked Tussock Moth.

0.8-1.3"

RUSTY TUSSOCK MOTH male is rust brown in color. Unlike the two above species, eggs are not covered with hair from the female. Larva has black head and black hair pencils on sides of abdomen.

0.8-1.3"

PINE TUSSOCK MOTH is a pest of Jack, Pitch, and Red pines, spruce, and sometimes fir. It is single-brooded, overwinters as hair-covered eggs. Male forewings are relatively well-marked.

1.3-1.5"

Western

Pine

Rusty

White-marked

LASIOCAMPIDS are a family of some thirty North American moths of medium size with stout hairy bodies. They are readily attracted to lights. Females are like the males but larger. The most familiar species are the tent caterpillars, pests of forest, shade, and orchard trees.

EASTERN TENT CATERPILLAR overwinters in "varnish-coated" egg masses around twigs. The larvae hatch in early spring, forming silky tents in crotches of limbs. They feed outside their tents, using them only for resting, unlike Fall Webworms which feed on the leaves enclosed within their silken webs. Apple and cherry are the most common food plants.

larva

cocoon

egg mass

1.0-1.8"

1.0-1.5"

CALIFORNIA TENT CATERPILLAR has a life history similar to the Eastern Tent Caterpillar's, but unlike that species, it includes oak among its many food plants.

California   Eastern

0.8-1.6"

FOREST TENT CATERPILLAR feeds on a variety of deciduous trees. The larvae do not make tents but spin silken mats on trunks or limbs where they rest and molt. The egg masses overwinter. There is one brood.

ZANOLIDS are closely related to the prominents (pp. 132-135). There are only three species in North America, all occurring east of the Rockies. Eggs are flat and wafer-like. The densely hairy larvae feed singly on leaves of trees and bushes. They make no cocoon but pupate in the ground and overwinter there.

1.3- 2.0"

larva

WILD CHERRY MOTH, or *Apatelodes torrefacta*, is common, attractive, and widespread. It feeds on many trees and shrubs but prefers Wild Cherry. There is one brood yearly.

Forest

GEOMETER, meaning earth measurer, refers to the way the crawling larva draws the rear of its body up to its front legs, forming a loop, and then extends its body again. This crawling pattern is associated with only two or three pairs of abdominal legs. Geometers are also called loopers, inch-worms, measuring worms, and span-worms. Most geometer moths have thin bodies and relatively broad, delicate wings. The females of some species are wingless. More than 1,000 species of geometers live in North America; some are serious pests.

female and eggs

larva

male
0.9-1.3"

Spring
Cankerworm
0.9-1.4"

larva

FALL CANKERWORM feeds on many kinds of trees but prefers apple and elm. The moths emerge late in fall when the wingless females lay eggs in masses on tree trunks. The eggs hatch in spring.

SPRING CANKERWORM larva differs from Fall Cankerworm's in having two rather than three abdominal prolegs, but, like them, pupates in the soil. The moths occur mostly in spring.

BRUCE SPANWORM occurs from N.J. to Quebec, and west to Alberta. The moth occurs in fall on Sugar Maple, poplar, beech, and other trees. The female is wingless. The larva resembles Spring Cankerworm in form but has six narrow white stripes.

0.9-1.4"

light

males

dark

0.9-1.4"

Cherry
Scallop-shell
Moth
larva

SPEAR-MARKED BLACK-MOTH has variable amounts of black and white. Larvae live together in nests of leaves, mostly birch and willow. It has two broods. Overwinters in soil as pupae.

CHERRY SCALLOP-SHELL MOTH is commonly seen in the larval stage on Wild Cherry leaves which it folds together. Double-brooded. The pupa overwinters in the soil.

0.8-1.4"

CURRANT SPANWORM is a pest of currant and gooseberry. Eggs are laid in early summer but do not hatch until the next spring. Larva pupates in the soil in May or early June.

WALNUT SPANWORM moths occur in early spring. The females are wingless. Larva feeds mainly on Live Oak but also attacks English Walnut and other fruit trees. Single-brooded.

1.0-1.3"

1.3-2.0"

larva

141

1.4-1.8"

LINDEN LOOPER moths occur in fall. The female is wingless. Eggs are laid singly or in small groups. They hatch in spring. Larva feeds on many kinds of leaves besides linden.

larva

1.3-2.3"

larva

PEPPER-AND-SALT MOTH occurs in late spring and early summer. Both sexes are winged. The larva, called Cleft-headed Spanworm, feeds on many deciduous trees. Pupa overwinters.

1.1-1.4"

larva

ELM SPANWORM as an adult is called Snow-white Linden Moth. Groups of eggs are laid in July on bark of trees, pass the winter there, and hatch in spring. Larva feeds on many trees besides elm.

HEMLOCK LOOPER feeds mostly on hemlock and Balsam Fir. Moths occur in late summer. Their eggs, which hatch the following spring, are laid singly or in small groups on bark or needles.

1.1-1.5"

Linden and Elm

Pepper

Hemlock

CHAIN-SPOTTED GEOM-ETER moths occur from Aug. to Oct. Eggs overwinter, hatching late in spring. Larva feeds mostly on shrubs and small trees. Pupae form on leaves in loose cocoons.

1.1-1.8"

1.5-2.0"

larva

LARGE MAPLE SPANWORM prefers maple and oak to its many other food plants. The larva resembles a twig. There are two broods. Moths occur through the summer. Pupa overwinters.

larva

0.8-0.9"

THREE-SPOTTED FILLIP is single-brooded. Moths occur in early summer. Larva is green with narrow, broken, white lines and a yellow stripe on each side of the back. It feeds on maple.

1.0-1.8"

CROCUS GEOMETER, or Cranberry Looper, feeds on many low-growing plants. Moths occur in early summer. They vary greatly in amount of wing spotting. Females are often spotless. Pupa overwinters.

143

0.8-1.1"

larva feeding

pupal case

BAGWORM, or Evergreen Bagworm, is common from Mass. and Kans. south to Fla. and Tex. Feeds mainly on evergreens as well as locust, sycamore, and willow. Eggs overwinter in bag. Moths emerge in fall.

BAGWORM MOTHS are named for the silken bag which the larva covers with bits of the food plant. When full-grown, it fastens the bag to a twig and changes to a pupa. The female moth is wingless and legless. She lays her eggs inside the bag. There are about 20 species of bagworm moths in North America.

CLEARWING MOTHS, with transparent wings, resemble bees and wasps. They fly in the daytime and feed at flowers. Larvae are borers in bark, stems, or roots of trees, or in stems or roots of smaller plants. A few of the 125 North American species are pests.

PEACH TREE BORER attacks stone fruit trees near the ground. It occurs in southern Canada and the United States. Color pattern varies throughout its range. It is single-brooded.

SQUASH VINE BORER occurs in most of North America except along the Pacific coast. Larva feeds in squash stems and is a serious pest. It overwinters in the ground; pupates in the spring.

male
0.8-1.4"

female

0.8-1.3"

144

0.8-1.5"   0.6-1.0"

SADDLEBACK CATERPIL-LAR, named for the oval brown spot on its back, has distinctive stinging spines. It feeds on various plants, including corn, rose, cherry, and Pawpaw.

SPINY OAK-SLUG also has stinging spines. Besides oak, it feeds on pear, willow, cherry, and other trees. The moth occurs in June. The number of green spots on the forewing varies.

SLUG CATERPILLAR MOTHS number over 40 North

American species. The larvae crawl like slugs; their thorax legs are small and the prolegs are replaced by sucking discs. The cocoon, made of dark brown silk, has a cap at one end which the emerging moth pushes aside. Larvae overwinter in the the oval to spherical cocoons.

HAG MOTH feeds mostly on shrubs. The larva, sometimes called Monkey Slug, has projections bearing stinging hairs along its sides. These hairs are woven into the cocoon.

SKIFF MOTH occurs in midsummer. Eggs are flat and wafer-like. Larva, without hair or stinging spines, prefers oak, Wild Cherry, and sycamore. Has distinct races varying in color.

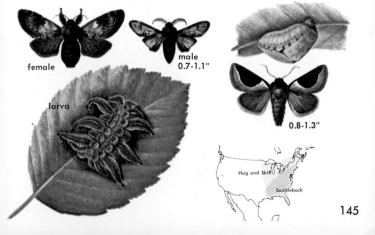

female

male
0.7-1.1"

larva

0.8-1.3"

Hag and Skiff

Saddleback

Ragweed Plume Moth
0.4-0.5"

lid

cocoon

larva

Puss Caterpillar
0.9-1.8"

PLUME MOTHS are named for the divisions into which the wings are split. The forewing may be separated into two parts, the hindwing into three. Ragweed Plume Moth occurs widely in the U.S. Larva and pupa are hairy. There are over 100 species in North America.

FLANNEL MOTHS are named for the texture of the wings. The larva, about an inch long when full-grown, is slug-like and bears stinging hairs. It has seven pairs of prolegs. The Puss Caterpillar of eastern U.S. is white when young. It overwinters in the cocoon.

LEAF ROLLERS make up a very large family, including many serious pests. The larva rolls a leaf or leaves together and lives inside them. Cocoons are made of thin, soft silk on or near the food plant.

SPRUCE BUDWORM, one of our worst forest pests, feeds mainly on firs and spruces. It occurs in Canada, northern U.S., and Colorado. Eggs are laid in midsummer. Larvae overwinter.

FRUIT TREE LEAF ROLLER occurs in apple-growing areas of the U.S. and Canada. Eggs are laid in masses on tree limbs, where they overwinter. They hatch early in spring.

0.7-1.1"

larva

pupa

0.5-0.9"

eggs

larva

1.5-2.8"

pupal case

LEOPARD MOTH, accidentally introduced from Europe about 1879, is a pest, mainly of elm and maples. One moth can lay about 800 eggs. Larvae become full-grown in about two years.

CARPENTER MOTHS are shaped like hawkmoths (p. 82). The grub-like larvae are borers in trees, even in solid wood. They pupate within the bored tunnels. When emerging, moths leave the shed pupal skin at the tunnel exit. They lay eggs on bark or in the tunnels from which they emerged. There are some 40 species north of Mexico.

CARPENTER MOTH is a pest of many hardwoods, mainly ash, oak, elm, locust, and maple. Eggs are laid on bark, often near wounds. This moth has a life cycle of from three to four years.

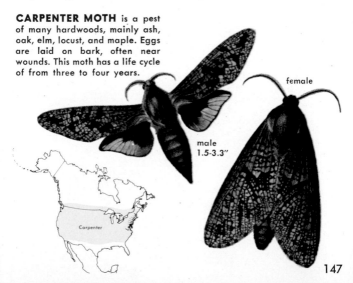

female

male
1.5-3.3"

Carpenter

147

0.6-1.2"

0.8-1.3"

GRAPE LEAF FOLDER is common from Mexico into southern Canada. Female has two white spots on hindwing. It is double-brooded. Pupa overwinters in folded grape or woodbine leaves.

ZIMMERMAN PINE MOTH occurs in no. U.S. and so. Canada, attacking pines. Larvae often feed and pupate on twigs infested by another insect. Eggs or larvae overwinter.

SNOUT MOTHS make up a large family of nearly 1,000 species north of Mexico. Mostly medium- to small-sized moths, they vary greatly in appearance. The main common feature is the snout-like projection in front of the head, composed of mouthparts called palpi. Many snout moths are important pests of crops and stored grain. The larvae usually live in the stems or rolled leaves of the food plant. Most kinds make thin cocoons.

EUROPEAN CORN BORER occurs in corn-growing areas of North America. Larva bores into stalks and ears. It also feeds on about 200 other plants, including dock, millet, pigweed, sorghum, and dahlia. Maturing in about a month, the larva pupates in the larval tunnel. Winter is passed as a larva.

male

female

0.8-1.4"

larva

pupa

SOUTHERN CORNSTALK BORER occurs from Md. and Kans. south to Fla. and Mex. and west to Ariz. Larva hibernates in corn stalks just above the roots. The species is double-brooded.

GREATER WAX MOTH is a nation-wide pest of beehives. Eggs are laid on or near the comb, on which the larva feeds. There are 3 broods. Winter is passed as a pupa.

CELERY LEAF TIER is widely distributed. It survives cold winters only in greenhouses. Besides celery, it is a pest of many garden and greenhouse plants, feeding and pupating in leaves.

GARDEN WEBWORM, a pest of alfalfa and other crops, ranges from S. America to so. Canada. Webbing is conspicuous in badly infested fields. Several broods occur. Pupa passes winter in soil.

INDIAN-MEAL MOTH feeds on many kinds of stored foods. The larva webs the materials together, making a thin cocoon. Indoors it breeds continuously.

0.4-0.8"

MEAL MOTH is common and widespread. The dirty-white larva lives in a silken tube. It feeds most commonly on cereals and cereal products.

0.5-1.1"

MEDITERRANEAN FLOUR MOTH feeds on whole grains and cereals but prefers flour, which the pinkish larvae web around them in masses. Since 1890 it has spread across all of North America.

0.6-1.0"

CASE BEARER larva lives in a thin, tough sac. When full-grown, it uses the case as a cocoon. Of more than 100 species, two of the most common, the Cigar and Pistol Case Bearers, are pests of apple and other fruit trees.

LEAF MINERS damage leaves. The tiny, flat larvae feed on the inner tissue. Most of the more than 200 North American species have shining scales and plumes. One of the best known is the Solitary Oak Leaf Miner.

0.4-0.5"

Cigar Case Bearer

Pistol Case Bearer larvae in cases

0.2-0.3"

Solitary Oak Leaf Miner larva inside of leaf

0.6-0.8"

larva

larva in seed

0.3-0.5"

STRAWBERRY LEAF ROLLER

occurs from the Atlantic west to Colo., Idaho, and so. Canada. It hibernates as a larva in a cocoon. The larva feeds in folded leaves. There are 2 to 3 generations.

MEXICAN JUMPING BEANS

are seeds, usually a species of croton from Mexico, that contain an active larva of a moth related to the Codling Moth. Larvae overwinter in the seeds.

OLETHREUTID MOTHS closely resemble the Leaf Rollers and Gelechiids (p. 152). There are over 700 North American species, many serious pests of farm and forest. Some differ greatly in their habits.

ORIENTAL FRUIT MOTH, of

the East and Southwest, chiefly attacks peaches. The larva bores directly into the twigs early in the spring; later generations enter fruit. Larva winters in a thin cocoon.

CODLING MOTH occurs

where apples grow. After wintering as larvae in cocoons, moths emerge in early spring. The larvae infest pears and other fruits of the apple family, also English Walnuts.

0.3-0.5"

0.6-0.8"

larva

larva

bud injury

pitch mass

0.5-0.8"

0.5-0.8"

EUROPEAN PINE SHOOT MOTH, a serious pest of Red, Scotch, Austrian, and Mugho Pines, lays eggs in early summer near the twig tips. Larva feeds in needles at first, later enters buds. Pitch forms over their burrows. Larva overwinters in buds.

PITCH TWIGMOTH emerges in late May and June. Eggs are laid on the twigs of Virginia and other hard pines into which the larva bores. Pitch masses form where the larva tunnels. The partly grown larva overwinters in twigs and feeds in spring.

GELECHIID MOTHS (below) number more than 400 species in North America. Many of these small moths are pests. Some larvae feed in stems. Others feed in rolled leaves or in leaves tied together. A few mine needles. Forewings are narrow, hindwings somewhat angular.

GOLDENROD SPINDLE GALL might be confused with the round gall of a fly. Before pupating in the gall, the larva makes an exit hole. Moths emerge through it in the fall.

ANGOUMOIS GRAIN MOTH is a serious pest of stored, whole-kernel grains, especially wheat and corn, throughout the United States. Some grain is attacked in the field at harvest time.

0.8-1.0"

0.3-0.8"

152

larva in gall

larva in corn

Webbing Clothes Moth
0.3-0.6"

larva

Carpet Moth
0.3-0.6"

Case-making
Clothes Moth

0.3-0.6"

TINEID MOTHS include more than 125 North American species. Some eat leaves, some fungus, and some wool fabric or fur. The Carpet Moths and Clothes Moths belong to this family. The Webbing Clothes Moth is most common. The Case-making Clothes Moth is darker. Its larva lives in a movable, open-ended case.

OTHER MOTHS The moths and butterflies on the previous pages represent thirty-six families of Lepidoptera. Some thirty more families exist in North America, including many inconspicuous moths. The following two moths are exceptions.

MIMOSA WEBWORM occurs on mimosa and Honey Locust in the East. It ties leaves together and feeds within the webbing. Double-brooded, it overwinters as a pupa in a soft, white cocoon.

YUCCA MOTH is essential for the Yucca's reproduction. The female moth carries pollen to the stigma, fertilizing the eggs which form seeds. Larva feeds in the seeds, pupates in spring.

webbing

larva

0.5-0.7"

0.8-1.3"

SCIENTIFIC NAMES

19 *Limenitis astyanax*
21 Pipevine: *Battus philenor*
Polydamas: *B. polydamas*
22 *Papilio polyxenes*
23 Baird's: *P. bairdii*
Anise: *P. zelicaon*
Indra: *P. indra*
24 Palamedes: *P. palamedes*
Alaskan: *P. machaon aliaska*
25 *P. cresphontes*
26 *P. troilus*
27 Eastern: *P. glaucus*
Western: *P. rutulus*
28 Two-tailed: *P. multicaudata*
Pale: *P. eurymedon*
Zebra: *Graphium marcellus*
29 Smintheus: *Parnassius phoebus smintheus*
Clodius: *P. clodius*
30 *Colias eurytheme*
31 Clouded: *C. philodice*
Pink: *C. interior*
32 Sara: *Anthocaris sara*
Falcate: *A. midea*
Olympian: *Euchloe olympia*
33 Orange: *Phoebis philea*
Cloudless: *P. sennae*
34 Calif.: *Zerene eurydice*
Southern: *Z. cesonia*
Little: *Eurema lisa*
35 Sleepy: *E. nicippe*
Fairy: *E. daira*
Dainty: *Nathalis iole*
Mustard: *Pieris napi*
36 Pine: *Neophasia menapia*
Great: *Ascia monuste phileta*
Giant: *A. josephina*
Florida: *Appias drusilla neumoegenii*
37 Checkered: *Pieris protodice*
Cabbage: *P. rapae*
38 *Danaus plexippus*
39 *D. gilippus berenice*
40 Eyed: *Lethe eurydice*
Creole: *L. creola*
Pearly: *L. portlandia*
41 Little: *Euptychia cymela*
Carolina: *E. hermes*
Gemmed: *E. gemma*
Georgia: *E. areolata*
Plain: *Coenonympha inornata*
Calif.: *C. california*
42 Riding's: *Neominois ridingsii*
Common: *Erebia epipsodea*
Common Wood: *Cercyonis pegala*
Nevada: *Oeneis nevadensis*
43 Gulf: *Agraulis vanillae*
Julia: *Dryas julia*
Zebra: *Heliconius charitonius*
44 Variegated: *Euptoieta claudia*
Regal: *Speyeria idalia*
45 Great: *S. cybele*
Aphrodite: *S. aphrodite*
46 Diana: *S. diana*

Nevada: *S. nevadensis*
Eurynome: *S. mormonia eurynome*
47 Silver: *Boloria selene myrina*
Eastern: *B. toddi*
Western: *B. epithore*
48 Baltimore: *Euphydryas phaeton*
Chalcedon: *E. chalcedona*
Silvery: *Melitaea nycteis*
Harris: *M. harrisii*
49 Mylitta: *Phyciodes mylitta*
Field: *P. campestris*
Phaon: *P. gorgone*
Pearl: *P. tharos*
50 Question Mark: *Polygonia interrogationis*
Satyr: *P. satyrus*
51 Comma: *P. comma*
Fawn: *P. faunus*
Zephyr: *P. zephyrus*
52 *Junonia coenia*
53 Painted: *Vanessa cardui*
West Coast: *V. carye*
54 Red Admiral: *V. atalanta*
American: *V. virginiensis*
55 Compton: *Nymphalis j-album*
Milbert's: *N. milberti*
Mourning: *N. antiopa*
56 White: *Limenitis arthemis*
Viceroy: *L. archippus*
57 Weidemeyer's: *L. weidemeyerii*
Lorquin's: *L. lorquini*
Red-spotted: *L. astyanax*
58 Calif.: *L. bredowii*
Goatweed: *Anaea andria*
Morrison's: *A. aidea morrisonii*
59 Hackberry: *Asterocampa celtis*
Tawny: *A. clyton*
60 Florida: *Eunica tatilista*
Ruddy: *Marpesia petreus*
Mimic: *Hypolimnas misippus*
61 Little: *Lephelisca virginiensis*
Swamp: *L. muticum*
Northern: *L. borealis*
62 Nais: *Apodemia nais*
Mormon Dark: *A. mormo mormo*
Mormon Light: *A. mormo mejicanus*
Snout: *Libytheana bachmanii*
63 Great: *Atlides halesus*
Colorado: *Hypaurotis chrysalus*
Gray: *Strymon melinus*
64 White-M: *Eupsyche m-album*
Edward's: *Strymon edwardsii*
Acadian: *S. acadica*
Southern: *S. favonius*
Red-banded: *Calycopis cecrops*
Coral: *S. titus*
65 Calif.: *S. californica*
Banded: *S. falacer*
Hedgerow: *S. saepium*
Striped: *S. liparops*
Sylvan: *S. sylvinus*
Olive: *Mitoura gryneus*
66 West.: *Incisalia nyphon*
Banded: *I. niphon*

Brown: *I. augustinus*
67 Western: *I. iroides*
Hoary: *I. polios*
Henry's: *I. henrici*
Frosted: *I. irus*
68 Great: *Lycaena xanthoides*
Ruddy: *L. rubidus*
American: *L. hypophlaeas*
69 Purplish: *L. helloides*
Gorgon: *L. gorgon*
Bronze: *L. thoe*
70 Harvester: *Feniseca tarquinius*
Eastern: *Everes comyntas*
71 Western: *E. amyntula*
Pygmy: *Brephidium exilis*
Dwarf: *B. isophthalma*
Common: *Celastrina argiolus pseudargiolus*
72 Marine: *Leptotes marina*
Reakirt's: *Hemiargus isola*
Acmon: *Plebejus acmon*
Orange: *P. melissa*
73 Saepiolus: *P. saepiolus*
Silvery: *Glaucopsyche lygdamus*
Sonora: *Philotes sonorensis*
Square-spotted: *P. battoides*
74 Hoary: *Achalarus lyciades*
Silver: *Epargyreus clarus*
75 Northern: *Thorybes pylades*
Southern: *T. bathyllus*
Long-tailed: *Urbanus proteus*
Golden: *Autochton cellus*
76 Sleepy: *Erynnis brizo*
Dreamy: *E. icelus*
Juvenal's: *E. juvenalis*
Martial's: *E. martialis*
Funeral: *E. funeralis*
Mournful: *E. tristis*
77 Checkered: *Pyrgus communis*
Grizzled: *P. centaureae*
Braz.: *Calpodes ethlius*
Common: *Pholisora catullus*
Sou.: *Staphylus mazans hayhurstii*
78 Uncas: *Hesperia uncas*
Cobweb: *H. metea*
Juba: *H. juba*
Indian: *H. sassacus*
Leonard's: *H. leonardus*
Golden: *Copaeodes aurantiaca*
Least: *Ancyloxypha numitor*
79 Long Dash: *Polites mystic*
Vernal: *Pompeius verna*
Peck's: *Polites coras*
Broken Dash: *Wallengrenia otho*
Fiery: *Hylephila phyleus*
Field: *Atalopedes campestris*
80 Hobomok: *Poanes hobomok*
Zabulon: *P. zabulon*
Roadside: *Amblyscirtes vialis*
Eufala: *Lerodea eufala*
Ocola: *Panoquina ocola*
Yucca: *Megathymus yuccae*
81 Atreides plebeius
82 Pink: *Agrius cingulatus*
Carolina: *Protoparce sexta*

83 Rustic: *P. rustica*
Five-spotted: *P. quinquemaculata*
84 Waved: *Ceratomia undulosa*
Catalpa: *C. catalpae*
85 Four-horned: *C. amyntor*
Hermit: *Sphinx eremitus*
Pawpaw: *Dolba hylaeus*
86 Elegant: *Sphinx perelegans*
Great Ash: *S. chersis*
87 Laurel: *S. kalmiae*
Apple: *S. gordius*
Wild Cherry: *S. drupiferarum*
88 Ello: *Erinnyis ello*
Abbot's: *Lapara coniferarum*
Bombyx: *L. bombycoides*
89 Big Poplar: *Pachysphinx modesta*
Abbot's: *Schecodina abbotti*
Sequoia: *Sphinx sequoiae*
90 Cerisy's: *Smerinthus cerisyi*
Huckleberry: *Paonias astylus*
Small-eyed: *P. myops*
91 Blind-eyed: *P. excaecatus*
Twin Spot: *Smerinthus geminatus*
Walnut: *Cressonia juglandis*
92 Nessus: *Amphion nessus*
Hydrangea: *Ampeloeca versicolor*
Hog: *A. myron*
Azalea: *Darapsa pholus*
93 Achemon: *Pholus achemon*
Pandora: *P. satellitia*
Lesser: *P. fasciatus*
94 Hummingbird: *Hemaris thysbe*
Bumblebee: *H. diffinis*
White-lined: *Celerio lineata*
Galium: *C. gallii intermedia*
95 Samia cynthia
96 Hyalophora cecropia
97 Ceanothus: *H. euryalus*
Glover's: *H. gloveri*
98 Columbian: *H. columbia*
Pandora: *Coloradia pandora*
99 Antheraea polyphemus
100 Callosamia promethea
101 C. angulifera
102 Actias luna
103 Io: *Automeris io*
Day: *Pseudohazis eglanterina*
104 Buck: *Hemileuca maia*
Nevada: *H. nevadensis*
105 H. oliviae
106 Honey: *Adelocephala bicolor*
Rosy: *Anisota rubicunda*
107 Orange: *A. senatoria*
Spiny: *A. stigma*
Pink: *A. virginiensis*
108 Citheronia regalis
109 Eacles imperialis
110 Ecpantheria scribonia
111 Acrea: *Estigmene acrea*
Isabella: *Isia isabella*
112 Garden: *Arctia caja*
Fall: *Hyphantria cunea*
113 Clymene: *Haploa clymene*
Arge: *Callarethia arge*
Virgo: *C. virgo*

114 Hickory: *Halisidota caryae*
Spotted: *H. maculata*
Pale: *H. tessellaris*
115 Yellow: *Diacrisia virginica*
Ranchman's: *Platyprepia guttata*
Dogbane: *Cycnia tenera*
116 Showy: *Holomelina ostenta*
Milkweed Tussock: *Euchaetias egle*
Bella: *Utetheisa bella*
117 Virginia: *Ctenucha virginica*
Brown: *C. brunnea*
Eight-spotted: *Alypia octomaculata*
Calif.: *Phryganidia californica*
118 *Ascalapha odorata*
119 American: *Acronicta americana*
Smeared: *A. oblinita*
Cottonwood: *A. lepusculina*
120 Black: *Agrotis ipsilon*
Pale-sided: *A. malefida*
Spotted: *Amathes c-nigrum*
W-Marked: *Spaelotis clandestina*
121 Pale: *Agrotis orthogonia*
Spotted-sided: *Amathes badinodis*
Glassy: *Crymodes devastator*
Striped: *Polia legitima*
122 Dark-sided: *Euxoa mesoria*
Striped: *E. tessellata*
White: *E. scandens*
Bronzed: *Nepheludes emmedonia*
123 Dingy: *Feltia subgothica*
Bristly: *Lacinipolia renigera*
Variegated: *Peridroma saucia*
Yellow-striped: *Prodenia ornithogalli*
124 Fall: *Laphygma frugiperda*
Armyworm: *Pseudaletia unipuncta*
Beet: *Spodoptera exigua*
Wheat: *Faronta diffusa*
125 Army: *Chorizagrotis auxiliaris*
Zebra: *Ceramica picta*
Cotton: *Alabama argillacea*
Green: *Plathypena scabra*
126 Alfalfa: *Autographa californica*
Bilobed: *A. biloba*
Celery: *Anagrapha falcifera*
Cabbage: *Trichoplusia ni*
127 Forage: *Caenurgina erechtea*
Lunate: *Zale lunata*
Green: *Lithophane antennata*
Dried: *Epizeuxis lubricalis*
128 Widow: *Catocala vidua*
White: *C. relicta*
129 Aholibah: *C. aholibah*
Penitent: *C. piatrix*
Tiny: *C. micronympha*
130 Locust: *Euparthenos nubilis*
Copper: *Amphipyra pyramidoides*
Pearly: *Euthesanotia unio*
131 White-veined: *Simyra henrici*
Stalk: *Papaipema nebris*
Corn: *Heliothis zea*
132 Poplar: *Ichthyura inclusa*
White-marked: *I. albosigma*
Tentacled: *Cerura multiscripta*

133 Yellow: *Datana ministra*
Walnut: *D. integerrima*
Sumac: *D. perspicua*
134 Variable: *Heterocampa manteo*
Saddled: *H. guttivitta*
Anguina: *Dasylophia anguina*
Elm Leaf: *Nerice bidentata*
135 Red-humped Caterpillar: *Schizura concinna*
Unicorn: *S. unicornis*
Rough: *Nadata gibbosa*
Red-humped Oakworm: *Symmerista albifrons*
136 Satin: *Stilpnotia salicis*
Gypsy: *Porthetria dispar*
137 White-marked: *Hemerocampa leucostigma*
Western: *H. vetusta*
Rusty: *Orgyia antiqua*
Pine: *Dasychira plagiata*
138 Eastern: *Malacosma americanum*
Calif.: *M. californicum*
139 Forest: *M. disstria*
Wild Cherry: *Apatelodes torrefacta*
140 Fall: *Alsophila pometaria*
Spring: *Paleacrita vernata*
Bruce: *Operophtera bruceata*
141 Spear-marked: *Eulype hastata*
Cherry: *Hydria undulata*
Currant: *Itame ribearia*
Walnut: *Coniodes plumogeraria*
142 Linden: *Erannis tiliaria*
Pepper-and-salt: *Biston cognataria*
Elm: *Ennomos subsignarius*
Hemlock: *Lambdina fiscellaria*
143 Chain-spotted: *Cingilia catenaria*
Large Maple: *Prochoerodes transversata*
Three-spotted: *Heterophleps triguttaria*
Crocus: *Xanthotype sospeta*
144 Bagworm: *Thyridopteryx ephemeraeformis*
Peach Tree: *Sanninoidea exiticea*
Squash: *Melittia cucurbitae*
145 Saddleback: *Sibine stimulea*
Spiny: *Euclea delphinii*
Hag: *Phobetron pithecium*
Skiff: *Prolimacodes scapha*
146 Ragweed: *Adaina ambrosiae*
Puss: *Megalopyga opercularis*
Spruce: *Choristoneura fumiferana*
Fruit Tree: *Archips argyrospilus*
147 Leopard: *Zeuzera pyrina*
Carpenter: *Prionoxystus robiniae*
148 Grape Leaf: *Desmia funeralis*
Zimmerman: *Dioryctria zimmermani*
European: *Pyrausta nubilalis*
149 Southern: *Diatraea cambidoides*
Greater: *Galleria mellonella*
Celery: *Udea rubigalis*
Garden: *Loxostege similalis*

INDEX

Asterisks (*) denote pages on which illustrations appear.

159

MEASURING SCALE (IN MILLIMETERS AND CENTIMETERS)